EGO IN EVOLUTION

EGO IN EVOLUTION

ESTHER MENAKER

AND

WILLIAM MENAKER

GROVE PRESS, INC. ■ NEW YORK

Library of Congress Catalog Card Number: 65-23855

Acknowledgment is due to Alfred A. Knopf, Inc.
for permission to quote from *Markings* by Dag
Hammarskjöld, Copyright © 1964 by Alfred A.
Knopf, Inc., and Faber and Faber Ltd.

First Printing

MANUFACTURED IN THE UNITED STATES OF AMERICA

This book is dedicated to our parents, our children, our patients, and our students. It is from them that we have learned the awesome power of human courage and aspirations.

At every moment you choose yourself. But do you choose *your* self? Body and soul contain a thousand possibilities out of which you can build many *I*'s. But in only one of them is there a congruence of the elector and the elected. Only one —which you will never find until you have excluded all those superficial and fleeting possibilities of being and doing with which you toy, out of curiosity or wonder or greed, and which hinder you from casting anchor in the experience of the mystery of life, and the consciousness of the talent entrusted to you which is your *I*.

Dag Hammarskjöld in *Markings*

▪ PREFACE

Nature is process.
—Clarence L. Herrick

THIS BOOK seeks to apply the unifying principle of evolution to the behavioral sciences, especially to psychology. In so doing, we are fully aware that in these areas more truth is observable than provable.

In 1942, Edith Hamilton wrote, "When the world is storm driven and the bad that happens, and the worse that threatens are so urgent as to shut out everything else from view, then we need to know all the strong fortresses of the spirit that men have built through the ages. The eternal perspectives are being blotted out, and our judgment of immediate issues will go wrong unless we bring them back."

Now, more than twenty years later, we are in even greater danger of losing our perspective. At a time when physical dangers threaten us, when a spirit of nihilism pervades the moral fabric of civilization, when men feel alienated from each other and from themselves, it is not easy to retain a long-range view of man's position. Yet, if we only were to look back and see how far we have come from our primitive beginnings—from beginnings that existed long before our appearance on the planet—then we might muster the faith to look forward and guess at the great distance we might traverse in the future.

In such a perspective, the present emerges as a passing moment in which the heritages of the past—biological, cultural, and psychological—are changed and molded to the needs of existing conditions, thus becoming the potential for the future. If in such transiency, retrogressive or destructive forces are in the ascendancy, they should not blur our vision of the general direction of man's advance. What is true of the perception of the movement of human history is no less true for the general direction of change in many individual lives. The conflicts of a given period in time must not blind us to the over-all potential for higher levels of integration.

In the course of many years of psychotherapeutic work, the authors have been impressed with positive, progressive strivings of patients to reach higher levels of functioning and of relating to others. This phenomenon as a common denominator of human existence assumed a primary position in our thinking, to which neurotic symptoms or sufferings, while needing to be treated, were secondary. Thus, our belief in man's capacity for progressive change derives from the observation either of such actual change or of aspirations toward it on the part of our patients.

In was in 1959 that this perspective on the driving, forward-moving nature of man's being merged with thoughts derived from our contact with ethology, which had contributed an evolutionary dimension to our understanding of behavior. The idea was not far off then that man's psychological make-up must be an outcome of evolutionary processes, fundamentally biological but ultimately psychosocial in nature, and must contribute to the further advance of these processes, thereby undergoing change itself. To perceive the phenomena of nature as processes in time is to create the opportunity for observing consistencies in the nature of their patternings and for noting the character and direction of change. This is the dimension which is implicit in an evolutionary approach.

The realization of the importance of this approach for the behavioral sciences would call for a functional framework within which to understand man—a framework in which biological, social, and psychological processes could be studied, as their interactions, operating under selection pressure, subserve survival, and create that specific evolutionary change which we call advance. It is within such a framework that we have attempted, in this book, to view the psychological life of man as an aspect of evolution as a whole, having distinguishing characteristics of its own, but sharing, in the fact of a specific vehicle for the transmission of traits and in the general direction of change, certain formal aspects of biological evolution.

Through the introduction of the concept of ego as at one and the same time the agent of change and that which is changing, we have endeavored to provide a nuclear unit for the study of that psychosocial evolution by which evolutionary processes of a nonbiological nature are effected.

The contribution of an evolutionary perspective to the understanding of the psychosocial life of man lies not only in an appreciation of the impetus and forward thrust of evolution in the sense of advance as it applies to his psychological make-up and his cultural products, but also in an awareness that the continuous interaction of environmental and organismic forces results in change in psychic processes from one historical period to another. Furthermore, the explanation for man's conflicts, his personality insufficiencies, and sufferings need no longer be sought exclusively in deterministically causal terms, through which responsibility is apportioned among early childhood experience, constitutional factors, or an interaction of the two. Man's psychic struggles, viewed in an enlarged evolutionary dimension, are in part an aspect of those struggles which constitute the very nature of the evolutionary process of life itself. Herein genetic givens, ontogenetic history, randomness of opportunity, striving for optimal realization, and unfolding of potentialities are at play in the service of expanding ego functions and survival. Such a conception could free the individual ego to assume responsibility for its optimal development. Thus, the psychological life of man is an open system, capable of change and progress, which characterizes the larger open system that is life itself.

In arriving at these conclusions, we have been influenced and inspired by many thinkers. Some of them appear in our references. Yet, the field is so vast that we are aware of a debt to many whose work bears on our own, who are either unknown to us or whom we have been unable to acknowledge because of the structural nature and limitations of our thesis.

It is a pleasure to express to our editor, Harry Braverman, the gratitude we feel for his grasp of the import of our thesis, for his tactful encouragement and editorial acumen. We have also profited from the suggestions of readers who remain anonymous to us. The staff of Grove Press has been most helpful in the preparation of the manuscript for publication.

Our son, Michael, Assistant Professor in the Department of Zoology at the University of Texas in Austin, has in innumerable ways functioned as guide and critic. We are indebted to him for his invaluable help in carefully editing those portions of the manuscript which deal with biological material.

It is with special appreciation that we thank Dr. Brock Chisholm, former head of the World Health Organization, and thus a pioneer in implementing psychosocial evolution, for his generosity in giving of his time and thought in reading the first draft of the manuscript.

The opportunity for contact with colleagues and students in the doctoral and post-doctoral programs of the Department of Clinical Psychology in the Graduate School at New York University has been a source of stimulation and has broadened our outlook in the psychological field.

Thanks are due to Mrs. Margaret Cleary of Danbury, Conn., for her meticulous and responsible services in preparing the typewritten manuscript.

Brookfield, Conn.
July, 1964

▪ CONTENTS

EGO IN EVOLUTION

1 · INTRODUCTION

WHEN A MAN makes an ax, builds a house, hunts his prey, talks with his neighbor, plans for the future, makes a decision, loves his wife and child, or is aware of himself doing any of these things and myriad others, his *ego* is functioning. Lost to him is the unknowing world of other creatures whose adaptive behavior evolved as a fugue between the outer environment and the living organism. For having evolved consciousness, he stands alone at the pinnacle of the evolutionary hierarchy, dependent largely on his own self-directed action for survival. A whole new world of mental experience opens up before him, a world of infinite variety and limitless possibility for expansion. To harness it for his own survival needs, man evolved a way of organizing the multiplicity of experience into a productive thought or a useful action. *Ego* evolved as the integrating and synthesizing process in the mental life of man.

Because each individual human creature is unique, his psychological make-up so complex and seemingly separate from the general, evolving stream of life, almost all efforts in the behavioral sciences have been directed toward understanding his ontogenetic development, his individual life cycle. Concern with his phylogeny, his evolutionary emergence as a species, has centered on man's physical characteristics, his neurophysiological evolution, and with overt behavior such as the making of tools, the development of language, the structuring of societal units and the development of culture, as these are outgrowths of physical evolution. There has been insufficient awareness that the emergence of the inner, regulatory aspects of man's mental life, of the purely psychological apparatuses, is an aspect of this same phylogeny.

In regard to the behavior of animals, Konrad Lorenz[1] has said that innate behavior patterns, those automatic, instinctual responses to environment that guarantee the survival of the species, are as much products of evolution as are morphological structures. We propose to extend this concept to man to include not only those automatic psychological responses which guarantee his survival, for example, the suckling reflex of the human infant, but above all the phylogenetically evolved capacity to consciously control behavior and inner awareness through the mediation of the psychic entity which we call ego.

The miracle of man is consciousness; but consciousness can only be experienced and implemented by means of ego. Only when I am aware of "I" can I know that the tree shelters me from the rain, that the sun warms me and all the earth, that another man may help or hurt me, that within limits I can do something to understand and mold my world, and ultimately myself. It is to the ineluctable forces of evolution that I owe my "I-ness," and the very awareness of this is part of the evolutionary process itself.

There is for man, then, no awareness without ego, and for both there are, in the mind of man, symbols. For in order to make use of impressions and experiences, man must remember them. He must build a psychic reservoir of recollections on which to base future action. In other words, he must learn and be aware of his learning. The human way of doing this is to give names to things. The awareness of man's total world is expressed in the symbols of language—those concerning external reality, those concerning others, and those concerning himself.

Thus, mind and its ultimate expression in conscious awareness and the symbols appropriate to this become a vehicle for a new way of dealing with the reality of the external and internal environment. Interposed between this world and man is a whole new world of his symbolic creation. It is over this world that ego presides.

Man's inner world of conceptualization, simply because it is intangible, is no less real than the world of physical reality. However, it has resulted in a partial estrangement from the immediacy of experience. The *idea* of the experience is for man the reality of awareness. The capacity for consciousness, in invoking the use of symbols for the functions of memory and anticipation, differentiates man's relationship to reality from that of other living beings. On the negative side, it makes conflict, anxiety, and sometimes even mental illness part of his lot. Nevertheless it is also the expression of and further cause of his psychological evolution. Obviously, the neurophysiological developments that led to the ultimate evolution of brain[2, 3] and then of consciousness could not be reversed despite the price to be paid for this awareness. Man could not go back to a preconceptual state. In order to master the inner world of his symbols, on which his survival in the physical as well as in the social and psychological worlds depended, he could only move forward to higher and more complex states in the organization of consciousness, i.e., to higher states of ego functioning. Ego, which had evolved, necessitated and gave the opportunity for its own further elaboration.[*]

In the course of the evolutionary history of man, through the operation of selection processes, all aspects of ego functioning led to a broadening of experience with its neurophysiological counterparts, e.g., an increase in the number of association areas in the brain,[†] thus to more awareness and intelligence, and finally to greater autonomy of ego itself. It is through the structuring of ego in the human personality that the possibility arose for the "social inheritance" of the experiences of the species and the consolidation of these inheritances in cultures. Through ego, man acquired a new medium for evolutionary change—not only for cultural change as we know it, but, because of the reciprocal action of social and psychological processes, for evolutionary advance in both of these areas.

We perceive the course of organic evolution retrospectively, for it is so slow that we are unaware of being in its stream at our given moment of life. We can only glance back and try to comprehend how far we have come. Not so with psychological evolution. Here, because man can so rapidly transform his environment and the interaction between it and himself, change can be noted within historical time, even

---

[*] Compare with Gerard's[4] conception of the evolving ability to evolve.
[†] "Notable in man is the extent of cortex which is associational compared with that which represents motor and sensory projection areas."[5]
For more detailed discussion, cf. Chapter VII.

within our own lifetime. Even when we do not perceive change as such, we experience the inexorable forward thrust of evolution in all human striving. It is the evolution of ego as the psychological "tissue" that has made possible man's psychosocial advance and has in turn been modified by this advance with which we are concerned in this volume.

Let us say a few words about our choice of the term "ego" and let us differentiate it from the concept, "the ego." Ego, as we conceive it, is a genetically determined character specific to man. In the psychological sphere, it parallels such concepts from the physical realm as opposable thumb, handedness, brachiation, bipedal locomotion, speech center—all those characteristically human acquisitions of the evolutionary process. Ego is that psychological capacity through which consciousness is organized and integrated, through which the person is set in function both physically and mentally, and through which adaptive thought and behavior is achieved. Ego has changed and is changing in quality and is increasing in complexity as the cultural history of man proceeds. Since these are fundamental changes in large sections of the human population through time and space, we feel justified in speaking of the evolution of ego.

"*The* ego," on the other hand, is, as the article implies, a particular, individual ego, the product of the life history of a particular person. The term in the field of dynamic psychology comes to us from psychoanalysis, namely from Freud's structural model of personality. The ego, according to Freud, is that part of the personality which, because of its close contact with the external world through perceptual consciousness, becomes gradually differentiated from the archaic "id," an unconscious reservoir of instinctual impulses. The concept of "the ego" has undergone changes and extensions in psychoanalytic theory, but it remains essentially an ontogenetic concept. Freud evinces in his conception of the "primitive mind"—a conception that is untenable in the light of modern anthropology—a concern with the evolutionary origins of personality. He sees man's link with the rest of the animal world primarily in the nature of his instinctual life. He does not, however, envisage the phylogenetic roots of ego first in the neurophysiological evolution of man and then in his further psychosocial evolution.

How the phylogenetic origins and the evolutionary push behind the emergence of ego have influenced the individual development of "*the* ego," and how each individual ego plays its role in the further evolution of ego are part of our theme.

The study of man's inner environment, of his psychic life, in itself a product of cultural evolution, emerged under the pressure of that adaptive need which called for understanding and mastery of himself as a vitally interacting part of the psychosocial biosphere in which his evolution takes place. The second half of the nineteenth century saw a tremendous movement toward systematization of these concerns in the behavioral sciences: psychology, sociology, and anthropology —all of which extended or replaced religious, philosophical, and metaphysical approaches to the understanding of man. The most profound, inclusive, and revolutionary theory of personality was contributed by Freud, and was significantly a product of psychotherapeutic endeavors. Through the introduction of the significance of the dynamic unconscious, the structuring of personality, and the distribution of psychic energy in the behavior of man, Freudian theory created the first usable model for a cohesive conception of human psychology, as well as a method, i.e., psychoanalysis, of dealing with its disturbances.

Undeniably great as is this achievement, it did not sufficiently take into account the full implications of the contributions of another great scientist whose work preceded Freud's by forty years, namely, the theory of evolution of

Charles Darwin. Freud saw the "id," the repository of all that was animal-like in man, as that part of human personality primarily linked with organic evolution. We, however, assume that the totality of man's capacities—for culture, love, guilt, ethics, and morality—all have their origin in the animal world, not in the sense in which Freud conceived of biological origin, i.e., as derivatives of sexual and aggressive impulses, but in the broadest evolutionary sense of hierarchical advance in the service of the most effective survival.

The resistance to Darwinian thought, to the principle of evolution applied to man's higher functions, i.e., to the emergence and further evolution of ego, is in part to be accounted for by the fact that man, after the initial struggle with and resistance to early Freudian discoveries, has been willing to share his lower, animal functions with the rest of the animal world, but not his higher self—consciousness and ego, and their by-products, culture and morality—which he considers his special prerogative.* These are undoubtedly human attributes or achievements; they have their origin, however, in the evolutionary stream of life, and a failure to place them in phylogenetic perspective often results in a confusion of ontogenetic with phylogenetic causality, in false assumptions regarding motivation, instinct, anxiety, and what is normal and pathological in the realm of behavior, and in inaccurate appraisals of the important role of the social setting in the development of human personality.

Our position in espousing an evolutionary theory for psychology is an attempt to bridge a gap created by Freudian theory on the one hand, which pointed to man's animal nature and conceived of it exclusively in terms of instinctual drives, and the rationalists and "psychologists of consciousness" on the other hand, who saw man as completely separate and

---

* In the Freudian theory of sublimation, cultural by-products are seen as derivatives of the instinctual drives.

different from the animal world because of consciousness. Neither saw that consciousness, thinking, speaking, creating, relating to others—all the necessary functions and actions of the human organism which in the psychological realm are synthesized through the function of ego—are an extension of the evolutionary processes that begin with the origin of life itself.

Such an undertaking seeks to integrate knowledge from several disciplines and focus it on a broader conception of human personality. The process of integrating knowledge, which in its organized form is science, proceeds in two major ways: through the collecting of data and the creation of theories. They are both essential to the advance of science, but in a strange way they are often in conflict: either data remain isolated and their larger implications are lost, or theories are based on too little data and run far afield of actual observation. These are the Scylla and Charybdis of science, and more especially of psychological science, which deals with the least quantifiable of data.

This book, nevertheless, will attempt to apply evolutionary concepts and principles to the field of psychology. There are points at which the theory overrides the provable data. We believe, however, that all science has evolved in this way, that theories are never the product of the accretion of individual data alone, but that they leap beyond what is given to the creation of something new which in turn becomes the point around which new detailed observations are made. We must be prepared at this point to sacrifice some accuracy for a new integrative principle, a new focus and point of departure.

Although we have spoken of the field of psychology, the observations and experiences from which we deduce our theory come from a specialized aspect of this field, namely, psychotherapy. One might question the validity of such an area of observation in a general theory of human psychological evolution. After all, we are observing the so-called "abnormal" rather than the normal; we are limited by clinical goals, therapeutic aims. How can we make more or less objective observations that would lend themselves to a unifying theory?

Here, a parallel can be drawn with the most exact of all sciences, physics. Robert Oppenheimer[6] has contrasted the fourteenth century view of matter with that of present-day atomic physics. The earlier, classical view held that matter was naturally at rest; our modern view has made it clear that the natural state of matter is one of constant movement. One cannot, therefore, observe a system without taking its dynamic nature into account. This truth is equally valid for psychology. It is precisely in the field of psychotherapy, in which we are dealing with a psychological organization in disturbance, that the dynamic interaction of forces is revealed. This enables us to study the nature of the component parts of the total personality and their integrative struggle with the external and internal environments. But more than this, we gain a view of the broader fact that the psychic life of man itself is in constant movement, not only in an individual developmental sense but also as an aspect of the total process of evolution.

■ REFERENCES

1. Lorenz, K.: Der Kumpan in der Umwelt des Vogels. *Jour. f. Ornith.* 83, 1935.
2. Clark, W. E. LeGros: *The Antecedents of Man.* Quadrangle Books, Chicago, 1960, pp. 255, 347.
3. Berrill, N. J.: *Man's Emerging Mind.* Dodd, Mead & Co., New York, 1955, p. 7.

4. Gerard, R.: Becoming—the residue of change. In Tax, S., Ed.: *The Evolution of Man, Evolution After Darwin*, Vol. II. University of Chicago Press, Chicago, 1960, pp. 255-267.
5. Washburn, S. L., and Howell, F. C.: In Tax, S., Ed., *op. cit.*, pp. 33-56. Quotation from p. 51.
6. Oppenheimer, R.: Analogy in science. *American Psychologist 11:* 127-135, 1956.

2 · THE OBSERVATION

EVOLUTION is the most inclusive concept of change in the world of living things. It is a process of change which tends toward improvement in the capacity of organisms to adapt to their environments. As change, it is a process; and as improvement, it is a process that is directed toward the future. All processes, however, require energy for their maintenance. Where does the energy for the evolutionary process come from?

There is no certainty about the answer to this question, but certain laws and theories may shed some light on the problem, and we will discuss them because of their bearing on our psychological observations.[1] Mathematical physicists tell us that in the system known as our universe the amount of free energy is decreasing, or, expressed in terms of the second law of thermodynamics, entropy (the quantity of unavailable energy) is increasing. Life, however, as a phenomenon within this universe, presents us with a different picture, for it has proved its capacity to evolve to levels of increasing complexity, adaptability, and efficiency. Life, as a specific organization of energy in the universe, is not running down, as is the physical universe. It is elaborating and organizing energy.*

When the first small fragment of living substance was wrested from the inorganic world, a new system of the organization of energy was born whose laws differed from those prevailing in the universe as a whole. Life could not only survive, duplicate, and thus perpetuate itself, but it had the capacity to make use of energy for evolutionary change.

However, life exists within the universe, for there is no organism without an environment. Therefore, although the laws governing the availability of energy seem different, and even contradictory, between the system "universe" and the system "life," there must be a relationship between them. Actually, the relationship can be expressed simply: Life draws upon the energy of the universe for its existence, it then makes use of this energy according to laws which govern its own biological system, and it does so at the cost of a loss of energy to the total system. In other words, the increase

---

* For the sake of clarity, it is perhaps important to point out that there exists no causal relationship between the increase in entropy, as stated in the second law of thermodynamics, and the use of available energy by living organisms. Quantitatively, the energy needed to maintain life is so small relative to the available energy that it cannot be a factor in the "running down" of the universe. This is clearly documented by Harold F. Blum.[2] According to the prevailing theory of physical science, the fact that the amount of free energy in the universe is decreasing is a fundamental law which operates independent of the existence of life.

in the complexity of organization of organisms is achieved at the price of a tapping of total available energy in the universe. This expenditure of energy has not only persisted over billions of years, but its momentum has increased, and has manifested itself in the evolutionary hierarchy, from the simplest unicellular organism to man. From the standpoint of the use of available energy, the process of evolutionary advance has not been efficient; but the measure of the power of the evolving life force lies precisely in the inexorable trend to increase biological efficiency in the face of the increase in entropy.

There is no doubt in the minds of those committed to a theory of evolution that man is the highest expression of the processes of evolution, representing life's tendency toward greater complexity and adaptability. This is true not only of his physical being, which includes his brain and nervous system, but of his psychic life as well. At a later point, we will discuss the evolution of the organic substratum of man's psychological make-up; however, at this point we wish to emphasize that his psychic life is a continuation, in non-genetic terms, of the evolutionary processes in the universe, and that it is impelled to advance by the same force responsible for all evolutionary movement.[3]

Man's nongenetic evolution has been recognized for some time through its manifestations in cultural advance. Having acquired through biological evolution, i.e., through the transmission of traits by specialized genetic material, certain indispensable physical structures and functions (e.g., bipedal locomotion, an opposable thumb, a large brain and nervous system*), man also acquired a capacity to verbalize, to think symbolically, and to remember. The creation and transmission of culture depends on these capacities. Implicit in this con-

---

* Cf. Chapter VII.

ception is the fact that man not only differs from the other animals in his capacity to create culture and that this in itself is an evolutionary advance, but that once the culture-creating process was under way, it too was subject to the forces of nonorganic evolution. Culture, from the dawn of man, has changed in the direction of man's increasing capacity to master his environment, so that there exists a hierarchical line of development which parallels biological evolution. That for the sake of clarity we have oversimplified the parallel should not be overlooked, however. The evolution of culture, for example, is subject to reversal, which is not true of organic evolution; the line of advance is, therefore, not always consistent, but the general, over-all tendency is toward greater complexity and efficiency, and the process is dominated by the same relentless momentum.

Cultural advance, since it depends so fundamentally on man's acquisition of psychological capacities, is inconceivable without a corresponding advance in these capacities. Evolutionists have been aware of this and have studied the evolution of psychological traits, using behavior as the most basic unit of psychosocial evolutionary change. Thus, for example, the social behavior of man has evolved beyond that of his primate antecedents, in that food-sharing, which does not exist among apes, became a necessity for survival and led to co-operation among men, and thus to social organization.[4] In the hierarchies that exist in ape as well as in human societies, there has been a change in the qualitative nature of the dominant individuals. In ape societies, the simple physical ability to overpower others and to appropriate desired objects is the dominance-creating factor; in primitive human societies, as among hunters and gatherers, elders are dominant and are respected for generosity and superior knowledge essential to the social life and survival of the group.[5]

Behavior, however, is only the overt manifestation of what

exists within the organism—whether structural, neurophysiological, or psychological—and its evolution must be the reflection of inner changes. In the continuous interaction between culture and behavior, what is actually changing is the nature and quality of man's personality structure. Specifically, we refer to the scope and sensitivity of his perceptions; his ability to integrate these with previous perceptions and experiences; his increasing capacity to remember because of improved integrative abilities; his increased sensitivity to and awareness of emotion, both his own and that of others; his greater reactivity to others and increasing complexity of interaction with them; and an increasing awareness of himself in the ever-enlarging framework of his environment as he comprehends and masters more and more of it. Furthermore, as the functioning of man's personality expands in terms of the faculties just enumerated, the dynamic interaction between these various parts also changes and evolves. Under the impact of evolutionary pressure, the subjective nature of experience and the objective relationship to reality are changing in the direction of advance. Man's personality, in phylogenetic terms, is being structured.

This psychological structure, while decidedly based on certain physical and neural prerequisites which may themselves be evolving, derives both its quality and its evolutionary momentum from the social environment in which man operates. Since this environment is itself continuously evolving, whether from more primitive to less primitive cultures in the anthropological sense or from one historical period to another, the personality of man is also subject to continuous and continuing evolutionary pressure.

Changes in personality can be observed in their large dimensions through the study of psychosocial changes. This involves making deductions about the nature of the prevailing personality structure within a given society. This is a valuable form

of observation and leads to conclusions about the broad outlines of personality in evolutionary perspective. For example,
a comparison of the attitudes of the dominant male population of England in the late eighteenth and nineteenth centuries toward women and children as reflected in the social
institutions, laws, and literature of a period characterized by
exploitation, abuse, and subjugation of these weaker elements
in the population, with those of the same population in the
twentieth century, would certainly show an advance in
personality in terms of the capacity to relate to and empathize
with others, a decrease in the fear of losing dominance, and
therefore an attainment of a higher ethical level. This is not
to say, of course, that these advances are reflected in the entire
male population, nor that, where they exist in individuals,
they necessarily herald evolutionary advance in all areas of
personality.

For the fine detail of personality evolution, however, we
need to extrapolate not from the general to the specific, as in
the study of psychosocial changes, but from the specific
(from the minute observation of a limited number of individuals) to the general (the population as a whole). Such
observations furnish an insight into the detailed interaction between culture and personality, the dynamic interaction
between parts of the personality, and the nature and force
of the evolutionary pressure to which the personality is subject. To make observations of this nature, one must be able to
see personality functioning in its totality. Nowhere is this
opportunity given to us more fully than in the psychotherapeutic situation.

Here, we see not only how a person learns, works, or
interacts with others, or how he gets angry, or what pleases
him, but the interaction of all these things and myriad others.
From his own accounts, and from what emerges unconsciously, we are able to reconstruct a developmental picture

of his life. We know something of what he was like as a child; we see the persistence of the child in him in his present-day functioning, his struggle against this persistence, and his aspirations for the future. It is worth noting that we have made such observations within the framework of a psycho-analytically oriented psychotherapy as opposed to psychoanal-ysis in the classical sense of that term. Robert W. White[6] makes the very valid point that the psychoanalytic method of observation, with its emphasis on "free association," is in most respects unsuitable for learning about the adaptive activities of the ego, since "it explicitly aims to reduce the activity of the ego" in the service of exploring the derivatives of un-conscious impulses. There is no doubt that the nature of such observations of personality cannot meet the standards of strict scientific observation; but this does not invalidate them. For strictly practical reasons, not all phenomena are subject to quantification, and indeed certain phenomena, and among them are psychological ones, become distorted when an attempt is made to measure them.*

Thus, the evaluation of behavior, or of a given personality trait, or of aspects of personality functioning have much to gain from observation within the framework of a totality of personality, and this opportunity is given to us in the psycho-therapeutic situation.

It is little wonder then that the first comprehensive, dy-namic, and workable theory of personality grew originally out of psychotherapeutic endeavor, namely, Freud's work with the neuroses. Freud's discovery of a dynamic uncon-scious operating in the psychic life of man has been compared with the revolutionary theories of Copernicus and Galileo. His assumption that personality included more than conscious

---

* A vivid account of the psychological as well as neurophysiological falla-cies derived from an oversimplification of learning theory is given in an extremely valuable methodological paper of D. O. Hebb.[7]

reaction and experience, that childhood was a highly impressionable period in the developmental life history, and that unconscious conflict had an independent, dynamic effect on behavior provided not only a theory of personality and of the neuroses, and a technique for treating the latter, but a new way of observing and understanding the psychology of man. The seminal nature of this contribution can be measured by what we would call its evolutionary impact, for it led not only to observations which confirmed some of Freud's own hypotheses and to extended work within the framework of his theory, but also opened the way for new questions, hypotheses, and vantage points for observation. This has been reflected in the work of those who followed: Rank, Adler, Horney, Sullivan, Fromm, Erikson, Fromm-Reichman, to mention only a few.

In working with people therapeutically, we have confirmed certain aspects of Freud's theory but have also become aware of the operation of factors which are not confined to the developmental history of the individual alone and thus go beyond his conception of personality. In other words, there are not only ontogenetic but phylogenetic factors as well. Since Freud has often been criticized for being too biological, an even broader biological viewpoint might seem a strange emphasis. We feel, however, that to the extent that such criticism was directed at Freud's failure to give sufficient weight to cultural factors in the formation of personality, it was justified. If, however, such criticism takes exception in principle to the conception of an interrelationship between biology and psychology, in fact, to the outgrowth of psychology and indeed culture itself from biological foundations, then we must disagree.

Freud's biological thinking is based primarily on a theory of instinctual motivation. Psychological phenomena take place because the organism is impelled toward action or thought by the wish for pleasure, which is defined broadly as the reduction of tension. In man, this "pleasure principle," as Freud calls it, is modified by his perception and awareness of reality which very early in life calls for the postponement or giving up of pleasure in the immediate sense, and the adherence to a "reality principle" which promises pleasure or substitute gratifications at a later point. The instinctual drives, which are the mental representations of physiological processes and which are sexual in nature in the broadest sense of that term, are responsible for behavior, although the individual ego is the executive organ for action. This ego is propelled by drives from behind and limited by societal demands from above. Thus, Freud saw the human ego, although biologically grounded and having some impetus toward survival, in a position between the millstones of instinct and internalized cultural requirements.

Furthermore, the ego according to Freud was an ontogenetic by-product of individual development. It became differentiated as a result of instinctual frustrations at early infantile levels of development. Although Freud paid lip service to a survival instinct vested in the ego, the ego itself only acquired a dynamic quality as a result of conflict; it seemed to have little propulsive force of its own that could be attributed to instincts of its own. Not only were all the normal phases of individual growth and development in terms of ego activity unaccounted for, but also the enormous panorama of man's mastery of nature, his scientific and creative activity, and the hierarchical increase in these areas were not related to ego drives.

In an attempt to correct this deficiency in the Freudian conception of personality, H. Hartmann[8] proposed a theory of a conflict-free ego sphere which gives room for the normal development of ego functions within the Freudian framework. A common meeting ground for developmental studies of personality and dynamic psychology is thereby created. There is an "embryology" of the ego in which certain functions are known to grow and develop at given times and in a certain sequence. This development depends on the neurophysiological nature of man and, while environmental stimuli (some optimal, others minimal) are essential for normal development, a predisposition for these developmental processes is accepted. In work with Albanian children, who are swaddled from birth, Charlotte Buehler[9] has also shown the inherent character of the development of normal ego functions. Whereas the motor development of these children occurs later and more slowly than that of the unswaddled children of Western cultures, once these children have been unbound the motor functions quickly catch up to the normal developmental level. This is not to say that there may not be other important psychological effects of the swaddling, but it does not interfere fundamentally with what are inherent, developmental ego functions, namely, motor control and coordination.*

In certain cases which come to the psychotherapeutic situation, we have† the opportunity of observing not only the inherent ontogenetic developmental pattern of the ego, but also a fundamental aspect of its phylogeny: its capacity to evolve. Although we will later discuss the criteria for such evolution, we now refer to evolution by psychosocial means as opposed to genetic evolution. However, the capacity for such evolution is conceived of as being itself the product of biological evolution and as serving fundamentally biological functions, in the broadest species-survival sense.

In order to make clear the nature of our observation and what we mean by the evolving tendency of ego, let us take a

---

* This is what Hartmann calls the sphere of primary autonomy.

† The question of the importance of the societal framework will be discussed below.

case in point. A young man of approximately thirty-five seeks psychotherapeutic help, not for the relief of any specific symptoms nor even for the amelioration of any more generalized unhappiness, but in his own words: "To function more efficiently, to express myself more effectively." We see at once, before we know anything more about him, that his motivation is expressed in terms of "advance" rather than cure. He is operating with an expanding self-conception rather than a static one. As we become acquainted with him, we learn certain important facts about his life. He is the only son and the youngest child of a Mediterranean immigrant family. Economically, the family might be classified as lower middle class; there was never any serious deprivation, yet the struggle for survival was acute, leaving the father, a small business man, little time or energy for other pursuits. There were some old-world cultural influences in the home, but the dominant tendency was toward Americanization. This expressed itself in the mother in strong, compulsive needs for cleanliness and in the idealization of the control of emotion as a character trait. Undoubtedly, these by-products of the conflict of two cultures influenced certain aspects of the boy's growth and development. He became deeply introverted and led an active phantasy life, which, when combined with his native sensitivity, intelligence, and talent, enabled him as an adult to function creatively in his work as a teacher of literature in a small college. His family helped him acquire the necessary college and professional training for his chosen career. Although he went through a fanatically religious period, characterized by a compulsive concern with the observance of ritual, he outgrew this aspect of religious experience, became a freethinker, and in his late twenties married a young woman outside his faith who in her own right had a professional career.

One might almost ask why the patient sought psychotherapy. There were a number of not very obvious reasons.

He had done a considerable amount of writing in the field of literary criticism and had had a modicum of success. Shortly before he came into treatment he had begun writing a novel, and in this undertaking met with surprises. Not that he suffered from a work inhibition common to so many writers, but that he was sometimes astounded by the violence and quality of emotion which emerged in his writings and which was in contrast to his restrained, poised conscious behavior. His fictional writing, therefore, was in too great a sense beyond his control and insufficiently integrated with his total personality. To some extent, this was also true of his relationship with other people. He was disturbed by a certain sense of detachment from them. There were also tendencies to be too dependent on approval, especially in regard to his writing and to become somewhat depressed if his work was criticized.

This is hardly an alarming picture of a personality disorder, and many individuals would be content to get along as best they could with whatever emotional handicaps exist in the psychic life of such an individual. But the case is significant in quite a different sense. Both in terms of this young man's actual achievements and functioning in life, and of his perceptions of himself, his self-evaluation, and his striving toward certain integrative personality goals, he illustrates what we have in mind when we speak of the evolution of ego.

Let us take the more obvious aspects of such an evolution. They exist first on a socioeconomic and cultural level. Within a societal framework that made self-expansion possible, he acquired a higher education and a vocational position which was much closer to an expression of his natural abilities and interests than was his father's vocation. It is important to note that his father had, in his own life, expressed a wish for a higher education and had for a short time gone to college. Circumstances had interrupted this endeavor, and he had never returned. One has the distinct impression that this was not merely fortuitous, but that personal drive and ambition had receded and found expression in a projection of these impulses onto his son. The son's ability to identify with these impulses of the father constitutes part of the mechanism by which his ego striving is set in motion.

It is important, in evaluating our patient's cultural and economic advance over his father, to be clear that in conceiving of this as an aspect of evolution we are not setting up a system of values. There is nothing inherently more advanced in being a college teacher as opposed to a small business man, *except as it more closely approximates the optimal functioning and expressiveness of this particular ego.* Thus, we would say that maximal self-realization is an aspect of ego evolution.

Since man's ego functions are of primary importance in meeting his survival needs, the increasing autonomy of these functions is crucial to a definition of evolution. The striving for autonomy is observable not only in the developmental history of the individual but also in the tendency of his ego to achieve higher and more complex forms of organization, integration, and expression, and to make these socially operative. In addition, his striving for optimal delineation of his ego is expressed in what he proposes to do about his inner environment. He seeks not only balance between conflicting parts of his personality but also new ways of integrating experience. He is psychologically on the move.

This is clearly expressed in the case of our patient. Vocationally, his life represents an advance over his father's. The growing autonomy of his ego is further expressed in his ability to break the bonds of the ritualistic societal structure into which he was born. He began to think independently. His choice of a love-object was dictated by his personal needs and tastes, not by the cliché of his milieu. He was thus able to select an individual who herself was more autonomous than his own mother. His self-awareness, evident in the consciousness that his emotional expressions were often inappropriately vehement, is of an unusually high degree and represents a decided advance over the preceding generation. His desire to understand this discrepancy and to master the emotion represents a new order of ego striving.

It might be said that these changes have nothing to do with evolution, that they are merely caused by sociocultural changes of which increased knowledge is an important part. But that is precisely the point. They are indeed caused by cultural change. In this case, the dissemination of psychoanalytic knowledge is an important ingredient of the change. It is when cultural change interacts with a readiness of ego to make use of such changes for its own advancement that an evolutionary step forward in the qualitative nature of ego is made. When we realize that ego is man's most characteristic organ of adaptation, then any increase in its capacity to synthesize, integrate, and regulate experience, any increase in its sensitivity to all aspects of environment, inner and outer, any increase in its expressiveness, in its capacity for learning, as well as for what has been learned, and any greater activation of its functioning must be viewed as an evolutionary advance in psychological terms.

The evolutionary nature of such advances in the ego integration of individuals is further confirmed by their inevitably, to a greater or lesser extent, influencing the population as a whole. They raise the general level of society to the extent that their advanced ego functioning is transmitted either through direct interaction with others or through their creative products. This is true of any individual who makes an advance, for it is expressed in some way within the limited sphere of his influence. The sphere of influence of the artist, the scientist, or the discoverer is immense; he can at times really raise the general level of culture and thus make possible for others new opportunities for ego expansion.

In the case of our patient, this was indeed so. As a gifted and sensitive individual, he was able to make use of cultural opportunities to bring about progressive changes in his own ego structure; as a talented teacher, critic, and writer, he was able to offer new experiences to others which might influence their ego expansion and expressiveness. That he sought psychotherapy for the express purpose of functioning more efficiently is indicative of an evolutionary impetus which, as we said earlier, is manifest in all aspects of the life processes, and which in this case, as in many others, creates our area of observation.

▪ **REFERENCES**

1. Schroedinger, E.: *What Is Life?* Doubleday, New York, 1956, pp. 67-73.
2. Blum, H. F.: *Time's Arrow and Evolution*. Princeton University Press, Princeton, N. J., 1955, pp. 94-95.
3. Medawar, P. B.: *The Future of Man*. Basic Books, Inc., New York, 1959, pp. 95-97.
4. Roe, A., and Simpson, G. G.: *Behavior and Evolution*. Yale University Press, New Haven, 1958.
5. Sahlins, M. D.: The social life of monkeys, apes and primitive man. In Spuhler, J. N., Ed.: *The Evolution of Man's Capacity for Culture*. Wayne University Press, Detroit, 1959, pp. 54-73.
6. White, R. W.: *Ego and Reality in Psychoanalytic Theory*. Psychological Issues, Vol. III, No. 3, Monograph 11. International Universities Press, New York, 1963, p. 13.
7. Hebb, D. O.: Alice in Wonderland, or psychology among the biological sciences. In Harlow, H. F., and Woolsey,

C. N., Eds.: *Biological and Biochemical Bases of Behavior.* University of Wisconsin Press, Madison, 1958, pp. 451-467.

8. Hartmann, H.: *Ego Psychology and the Problem of Adaptation.* International Universities Press, New York, 1958.

9. Buehler, C.: *From Birth to Maturity.* Kegan Paul, Trench, Trubner & Co., Ltd., London, 1935, pp. 35, 84-85.

3 . THE WELLSPRINGS OF MIND

A TRUTH is valuable only as it illuminates past truths or points
the way to the discovery of future ones. Thus, science
advances within the framework of the thinking of a given
period, at the same time evolving new ways of thinking about
phenomena. If it fails to do this and to establish unifying
principles, it becomes merely a repository for collected facts.

The concept of evolution is such a unifying principle.
Primarily, it is a biological concept aimed at an explanation of
the origins of the varieties of living organisms and finally of
the origin of man. However, while it is interesting to know
about origins, these facts in themselves would not have had
so enormous an impact on the field of biology were it not

for the fact that with the idea of evolution came a new way of viewing biological phenomena. An organism was no longer a closed system, but one interacting with the external environment, with its inner environment, with other organisms, and having the potentiality for evolving under the pressure of new environmental conditions.

Evolution has been studied from two major points of view: the biological, including the evolution of neurophysiological structures and functions, and the sociocultural. To date, the first of these has been the most extensive, for it has included the evolution of life itself from the inorganic, the evolution of species, and finally the evolution of man. The biological study of the evolution of man has led inevitably to the consideration of the human mind as a product of evolution. Here, the evolutionists have concerned themselves with the evolution of the brain and the nervous system, with the increase in intelligence, the more organized and efficient development of functions such as locomotion, manipulation, speech, symbolic representation. The interaction of the evolution of the brain and behavioral evolution has been studied and the by-product of this interaction, "culture," has been recognized as an outcome of the biological evolution of man, and as having an evolutionary life of its own on a nongenetic basis.* The evolution of cultures has been studied, and the effects of culture on the further sociocultural evolution of man, as well as on his personality, have been inferred.

In this picture of man's evolution, there is a gap created by the failure to identify, as an area for scientific investigation,

---

* Julian Huxley[1] states the following:

". . . I see human history as a recent and very special outgrowth of biological evolution."

". . . the main unit of evolution in the human phase is not the biological species, but the stream of culture, and genetic advance has taken a back seat as compared with changes in the transmissible techniques of cultural advances."

a specific psychological evolution, and to distinguish it from ontogenetic psychological development as well as from socio-cultural evolution.

The evolution of mind to the proportions of human intelligence, the process of encephalization,[2,3] with all its products of elaborated function, is not in itself psychological evolution. *It is not the evolution of man's personality as such,* with its increasing complexity of intellectual and emotional experience, although it forms the absolutely necessary organic basis for it.

The fact of our biological evolution is generally accepted. Science has demonstrated with sufficient conviction, if not absolute proof, that living matter evolved from the nonliving, that the first living things were extremely simple, and that increasingly complex forms of life evolved from these. The fossil record gives us a picture of the evolutionary continuum of life on our planet.[4] In an ever-changing environment of gross geological changes, climatic upheavals, and minute differences, life could only maintain itself by evolving. A never-ending process of interaction between outside forces of the environmental world and living organisms was set in motion when life began.

The full import of the fact of organic evolution is difficult to grasp for several reasons. First, the time span involved from the first appearance of life to its evolution to more complex forms in the vertebrates, then mammals, primates, and finally man, a period of approximately two billion years, is so enormous as to be almost inconceivable. Not that we do not think in terms of an even greater time span, as for example in astronomy. But in the case of evolution, we are dealing with a process of which we are a part; therefore, the time involved is something with which we must attempt to identify; it is not just an abstraction. Second, we are not absolutely certain of how evolution took place, although we know many important facts about it and have today a generally accepted, convincing theory of it. This theory is referred to as the modern synthetic theory of evolution. Fundamental to it are the principle of natural selection introduced by Darwin and the mutation theory of De Vries. "The basic framework of the theory is that evolution is a two-stage phenomenon: the production of variation and the sorting of the variants by natural selection."[5]

For the purpose of bringing into relief these fundamental concepts, we shall greatly simplify our explanation. In the process of reproduction by which organisms perpetuate their kind, they do not simply duplicate themselves. Variants are created either by slight genetic changes known as "mutations" or through the operation of processes of genetic recombination within species populations.

The pressures of an ever-changing environment continually interact with these variants, selectively favoring the survival and reproductive success of those individuals within a population who represent the best of possible alternative adaptations to existing conditions.

In 1947, Simpson[6] made a vivid analogy which helps us to envisage the operation of the processes of natural selection:

How natural selection works as a creative process can perhaps best be explained by a very much oversimplified analogy. Suppose that from a pool of all the letters of the alphabet in large, equal abundance you tried to draw simultaneously the letters c, a, and t, in order to achieve a purposeful combination of these into the word "cat." Drawing out three letters at a time and then discarding them if they did not form this useful combination, you obviously would have very little chance of achieving your purpose. You might spend days, weeks, or even years at your task before you finally succeeded. The possible number of combinations of three letters is very large and only one of these is suitable for your purpose. Indeed, you might well never succeed, because you might have drawn all the c's, a's or t's in wrong combinations and have discarded them before you succeeded in drawing all three together. But now suppose that every time you draw a c, an a, or a t in a wrong combination, you are allowed to put these desirable letters back in the pool and to discard the undesirable letters. Now you are sure of obtaining your result, and your chances of obtaining it quickly are much improved. In time there will be only c's, a's, and t's in the pool, but you probably will have succeeded long before that. Now suppose that in addition to returning c's, a's, and t's to the pool and discarding all other letters, you are allowed to clip together any two of the desirable letters when you happen to draw them at the same time. You will shortly have in the pool a large number of clipped ca, ct, and at combinations plus an also large number of t's, a's, and c's needed to complete one of these if it is drawn again. Your chances of quickly obtaining the desired result are improved still more, and by these processes you have "generated a high degree of improbability"—you have made it probable that you will quickly achieve the combination cat, which was so improbable at the outset. Moreover, you have created something. You did not create the letters c, a, and t, but you have created the word "cat," which did not exist when you started.

The "purposeful combination" of letters to create the word "cat" has its analogue in the "purposeful combination" of genes which the pressures of natural selection impose upon organisms.

Although scientific inquiry eschews the concept of "purpose" in a teleological sense, the question of the function of the "purposeful combinations" as they seem to define the directional process of evolution is not entirely answered by the concepts of survival, adaptation, or reproductive success. The complete meaning of the term evolution must take into account the factors of progress and of potentiality.

Julian Huxley[1] deals with these factors in his definition of "biological improvement." He says: "Most improvement is specialization—it is improvement merely in relation to some restricted way of life or habitat. Some improvements, however, merit the name *advance*. That is so whenever the *efficiency* of any major function of life is increased, whenever a higher and more integrated organization is achieved, whenever any radically new piece of biological machinery is evolved. . . . So we can conveniently define biological progress as improvement which permits or facilitates further improvement; or—as a series of advances which do not stand in the way of further advances."*

We see at once that evolution, as the word itself indicates, implies movement (but not random movement) in the general direction of advance along a line (with many branchings) that represents a series of increasingly efficient organisms. In other words, by such a definition we would speak of an advance in terms of greater efficiency of major life functions, as we proceed from Protozoa to Metazoa, from invertebrates to vertebrates, from fish to reptiles, to birds, to mammals, to primates, and finally to man. In speaking of evolutionary progress, Simpson also makes the important point that "the concomitants of evolutionary progress should be sought in *function* and in structure as related plainly to *function*."*[7]

For the understanding of human evolution as it eventuates in a nonorganic, sociopsychological process, the appreciation of the specific organic prerequisite for this evolution is important. We refer here to the evolution of the human nervous system which represents evolutionary progress expressed in "increased awareness and perception of the environment and increased ability to react accordingly."[7]

One of the essential criteria then for the concept of evolution is *advance*, not in the sense of specialization alone, i.e., a more efficient functioning of existing life functions in a restricted medium, but in the sense of an increase in the

---

* Italics ours.

capacity to survive and reproduce in an increasingly complex biosphere. Thus, one cannot say that an amoeba is less well adapted to its biosphere than an ape to its biosphere, but one can maintain that the number and kinds of circumstances to which the ape is adapted is infinitely greater and that the range of flexibility of this adaptation is greater. The tendency of organisms to burst the boundaries of existing biospheres, to increase the scope of adaptability, and to evolve in the direction of greater integration with the environment is an essential characteristic of advance in evolution.

The living organism is in a constant state of interaction with the environment, both on the level of its individual functioning, and on the level of its evolutionary functioning, i.e., its membership in a genetic population which is advancing, or has the potentiality to advance. This interaction would seem to have two seemingly contradictory aspects: an adaptation in the direction of specialization for and integration with the environment, and a movement as a result of environmental pressure beyond the existing environment to a new biosphere, to a new "niche," as the ecologists call it. The response of organisms to environmental pressure and opportunity in terms of a general advance in efficiency and complexity of organization derives in part from the fact that the evolutionary process operates directionally in time, i.e., that "change occurs on the basis of what is already there."[4] However, it is important to bear in mind that in the very nature of this irrevocability of "what is already there," there lies the potentiality for improvement. The process of natural selection not only ensures adaptation to given environmental conditions, but "by selecting simultaneously for the preservation of genetic variability," it "is ready in each generation to jump off in new directions."[5] In this tendency is implied the evolutionary exploitation of adaptive potential which is augmented as evolution advances.

The unicellular organism, in the nature of its adaptation to its environment, is dependent on a narrow range of external conditions, temperature, light, etc., for survival. Its adaptation is highly specialized. When, in the course of evolution, such specialization gives way to an adaptation through specialized parts of the organism to specific aspects of the environment, the organism as a whole, while adapted to, is nevertheless freer from the environment than its more generally specialized ancestor.

It is this tendency of living things in the course of their evolution to expand their adaptive potential in the direction of a less specific adaptation to the environment that finds its ultimate expression in man. Man's organic evolution represents a freedom from the environment that had never before been reached, for man is not only adapted to an ever-expanding environment, but also his particular evolutionary development has led to a shift from "adaptation to" to "mastery of" that environment. Evolutionists have long been aware that the evolution of the upright position, bipedal locomotion, the opposable thumb, the enormous elaboration of the sensory apparatuses, the brain and nervous system, the growth of intelligence, the development of speech, and the capacity for symbolic thinking have given man a plasticity of adaptation that includes increased control of the environment.

This end-product in man represents the most complex elaboration of one important tendency that exists all along the evolutionary line. It is the tendency among others of organisms to evolve in such a way that their adaptations for survival represent not only an adjustment to environment but a greater independence of specific environment.

Up to this point we have concerned ourselves with biological, i.e., organic evolution—the evolution of structures and their corresponding functions which are genetically transmitted. In the course of evolution, there has evolved, along with organs for breathing, circulation, locomotion, digestion, etc., a structure or an organ, or system of organs for reactivity to the environment—receptor, conductor, and effector in some form—so that the organism can deal appropriately with external conditions. Whether this receptor is the primitive network of nerve-like fibers in a one-celled animal or the highly complex nervous system in the vertebrates, or finally the brain of man, *its evolution is the expression of the development of mind as a part of organic evolution.* In this sense, the evolution of mind is the evolution of nervous control—of those apparatuses which mediate between the organism and its environment, and regulate the responses of various parts of the organism to each other. Whether these regulatory processes are of the simplest form, as in tropisms —such as the tendency of green plants to grow toward the light—or are more complex instinctual behavior responses, or involve the capacity to learn, organically they are based on the genetic inheritance of certain structures which carry the potentiality for a given patterned response.

In the course of evolution, these structures or apparatuses for responsiveness have advanced to ever higher levels. Therefore, it must follow that the *nature of experience* has also evolved from simple to increasingly complex responses of the organism to the outside world. In subhuman forms, this has manifested itself in increasingly complex forms of behavior. (We do not wish to be misunderstood: Behavior as experience does not necessarily imply the awareness of this experience.) All along the animal evolutionary scale, we see the evolution of nervous apparatuses which increase the organism's reactivity to the external environment and to the inner metabolic environment, and which are paralleled by increasingly complex behavior patterns.

The stentor, a simple one-celled animal, has no differentiated nervous apparatus but responds to external irritants with its entire organism. If nonedible particles are dropped on it by an experimenter, it will at first respond as if they were food, then try to turn away from them by bending its body and reversing its cilia; when this fails as an avoidance reaction, it will withdraw into its protective tube. If this is repeated, the final response becomes the first, showing that there has been learning on some simple level.

In the rat, the nervous apparatus is highly differentiated and both behavior and learning are of a high order. For example, it is possible to condition a rat to press a lever which will release food pellets only when a light is turned on, and to avoid doing so when it is dark.[8, 9]

Chimpanzees, on the other hand, have reached such a high level of brain and nervous system development that they are able to solve certain kinds of problems by methods other than trial and error, e.g., the reaching for food by putting two sticks together and spearing it with this tool. They have some capacity to "think," to deal, if even on a simple level, with concepts.[8]

In man, the enormous leap in the development of brain and nervous system has resulted in consciousness, in the capacity to symbolize experience, to store it as memory, and to communicate it. These experiential evolutionary changes have manifested themselves in two important ways: (1) through the evolution of culture and (2) through the evolution of psychic apparatuses.

That the evolution of culture introduces an entirely new dimension to the evolutionary process as applied to man has been ably pointed out by evolutionists (Simpson, Huxley, Berrill, etc.), anthropologists, and psychologists. The important emphasis here has been that because of man's capacity to store information by other than genetic means, he can transmit and perpetuate experience through tradition. This, together with his ability to apply intelligence to the mastery of environment, creates a structured behavioral continuity which we call culture.

The function of culture is basically to ensure the survival of the human species. In this sense, it replaces the built-in behavioral survival mechanisms of lower animals. Just as life itself has filled every available niche in the world through the operation of evolutionary processes, so the deployment of men over the face of the earth in all types of environment was made possible by the evolution of his capacity for culture. Culture is the expression of adaptive processes in relation to three distinct aspects of the environment: the *physical,* as a consequence of which we have the particular economy of a given culture and the artifacts pertaining to it (hunting [nomadic], fishing, agriculture, etc.); the *social,* as a result of which we have particular social structures and interpersonal interactions within a given culture, i.e., the family form, social hierarchies, governments, etc.; and the *psychological,* as a result of which we have the products of the attempts of man to integrate and give expression to his verbal concept regarding the world about him and his own inner world. Thus, we have religious forms, myths and legends, rituals, art forms, and written language. It is obvious that these aspects of culture interact and mutually influence each other. A hunting economy is likely to have a characteristic social structure as well as characteristic psychological by-products. But it is of special importance to note that the psychological aspects of a culture are influenced by the culture, and in turn influence the development of the culture. Thus, there is a continuous oscillation between the environment, constituting the external cultural form, and the inner psychological environment, which is analogous to the continuously adaptive processes which go on in the organic world between the living organism and its external environment.

Culture, since man is a social animal, must be as old as man, which in evolutionary time is recent. Yet, within the relatively short period of the existence of culture, one can distinguish an evolutionary development characterized first of all by a tremendous jump from so-called primitive cultures to civilizations. Within both groupings, there is tremendous diversification, just as there is within the species. The study of primitive cultures makes clear the very intimate relationship between the culture form and the environment in which it grew up. The Arctic culture of the Eskimos, in terms of its economy (hunting and fishing), its artifacts, and housing, represents quite clearly the limitations imposed by the geographic environment. These limitations, as they failed to permit among other things the development of agriculture, influenced the social development of the culture and maintained it at a Stone Age level. Because this interaction becomes much more intricate in the case of civilizations, it is not so apparent, but we must deduce that the same evolutionary forces are at work.

The distinction most generally made between primitive culture and civilization is the presence in the latter of written language and therefore of recorded history. This way of accumulating and transmitting information and experience increased enormously the rate at which cultural evolution could take place. The projection of the verbal symbols into the permanent form of written language resulted in the creation of an ever-changing environment in which an increasing number of individuals from the total population participated. This changed and changing environment then in turn reacted upon individuals and populations.

What are the discrepancies between primitive cultures and civilizations that are relevant to an application of the concept evolution to culture? First, it would seem that primitive cultures, as they exist today, are like the "living fossils" of biology. They represent such a felicitous cultural adaptation of man to his environment within a narrow, relatively unchanged niche that they themselves have remained unchanged. It follows then that cultural evolution, like biological evolution, proceeds under environmental pressure.

It is known that cultures, primitive as well as civilized, have become extinct. In this, they parallel the extinction of biological species, and their extinction has taken place for similar reasons: Their cultural adaptations have been too rigidly specific to meet the needs of changing environments, or they have been unable to compete with more dominant cultural forms with which they have come in contact, or a combination of both.

There can be no doubt then, from the mere fact of the existence of primitive as well as of more complex cultures, as well as from the fact of extinction, that on a nongenetic basis culture has evolved and is evolving and that this evolution is characterized by advance in the direction of greater adaptability to more varied environments and by a more accurate perception of and mastery of this environment.

Culture is the tangible expression of the evolution of man's brain and nervous system; it is the product of this evolution and it may in turn reciprocally influence this evolution. But what has happened meanwhile to the mind of man? Can we be content to study the evolution of mind only in terms of its neurophysiological basis, or of its product, culture? The inner psychological representation of the biological evolution of the nervous system, i.e., man's psyche, must have undergone, and must still be undergoing, an evolutionary process of its own.

Simpson, in an article[10] on the influence of Darwinian thought, makes the comparison between the world picture of the Kamarakoto Indians and our own, since the introduction of the concept of evolution:

The conceptual world of the Kamarakotos is more or less similar to that of ancient, truly primitive men . . . in space, a saucer a few miles across; in time, from a few years to a few generations back into a misty past; in essence, lawless, unpredictable, and haunted. Anything might happen. The Kamarakoto Indians quite believe that animals become men and men become stones; for them there is neither limitation nor reason in the flux of nature. There is also a brooding evil in their world, a sense of wrongness and fatality that they call *kanaima* and see manifested in every unusual event and object.

It is apparent that the Kamarakoto Indians live in an extremely narrow world with many misconceptions about causality regarding universal phenomena and their place in the world. Our world, since Darwin, has been broadened to include our relationship to all living things, which in turn have a common origin. We are aware of the interaction of external environment and the living organism in a way which was not possible before evolutionary thought. Now the difference between ourselves and the Kamarakoto Indians is not just in knowledge. If we were to leave it at that, we would merely be describing a difference in cultures. The point which Simpson makes is that they have a *world picture* different from ours. A world picture is an inner, psychological phenomenon, so that it becomes clear that between the primitive Kamarakoto Indians and ourselves there has occurred the evolution of a psychological process—namely, of the way of perceiving and comprehending the outer world and of integrating these perceptions into an inner specific world picture. We would carry the thought still further: when the world picture changes, there must be a corresponding change in the *self-conception.* The way we understand the world around us must inevitably influence the way we see our place in it. The projective tests in psychology (Rorschach, TAT) have made this very clear: What exists within us as psychological state influences our perception of the outside (test material), and, therefore, the perception of the outside becomes a measure of an inner condition.

The evolutionary step which took place between a primitive people like the Kamarakoto Indians and ourselves is therefore not only a cultural one, and not only a psychological one in terms of an understanding of the world, but a psychological one in terms of a different level of self-conception.

This small but very illustrative example is not only valuable in demonstrating an evolutionary process, it also points up more specifically than is apparent at first glance what exactly is evolving. Is it just the world picture itself, or the self-conception which is an interacting part of that world picture? Why do we arrive at a world picture? What is its function? It is not just curiosity that has impelled man from the beginning to ask questions about his world and to try to find meaning in it. Nor is this impulse merely a by-product of anxiety, although both curiosity and anxiety play a secondary role in the search for meaning.

What is involved in a primary way has a much closer link with the biological. *When consciousness evolved as the highest expression of the evolution of nervous control, it was inevitable that an integrating principle evolve in conjunction with it.* Man could not have experienced awareness without having evolved a way of organizing, integrating, co-ordinating the "different awarenesses," otherwise his psychological state would have been chaotic. A most dramatic example of this is described by J. Z. Young[11] when he cites cases of individuals who had been blind and whose vision had been restored through surgical intervention. "Vision," however, did not constitute "seeing," and often for many individuals there was a relatively long, chaotic period during which visual images were not organized into a seeing experience and during which there was no meaning, therefore, in the awareness.

The way of organizing and integrating the experiences of consciousness (as well as experiences that are unconscious) was made possible through the existence of a psychological apparatus which we call *ego*. It evolved biologically as a concomitant of consciousness and, like consciousness, is based in neurophysiological evolution. We can expect to find, then, in the hierarchy of living organisms, precursors both of consciousness and of ego, and in this sense we can say that "mind" has existed from the beginning of life. However, when we arrive at the human species, the emergence of consciousness and its elaboration into verbal symbols which can be retained and transmitted introduces the dimension of psychological function on a new qualitative level. This is true, perhaps to an even greater degree, of the evolution of ego as an integrating apparatus. In the subhuman animal world, the integrating function is performed by innate behavior patterns.[12]

We seem to have come a long way from our example of the Kamarakoto Indians and their world picture. Now, a world picture is an elaborate, sophisticated, abstract way of integrating many experiences. The objective validity of the world picture is irrelevant at this point. What is important is that it represents an attempt at synthesis, at integration, and as such is a product of ego function. What has evolved, then, in the leap from the narrow world picture of these primitive peoples to our own, is not only a greater capacity for knowledge, comprehension, and investigation, but also an inevitable corollary of these: a much more complex process of integration, which is a function of ego. What we have in common with the Kamarakoto Indians, and all peoples for that matter, is the ability to organize and integrate our perceptions—an ability which expresses primarily biological, adaptive, survival functions. This ability, residing as it does in the ego apparatus, became itself, in the course of human evolution, subject to a nongenetic evolutionary process—a process both cultural and psychological. It is because of this evolution of ego that our world picture as well as our self-picture has advanced so far beyond that of primitive peoples.

By way of illustration, we have dealt with only one aspect of the evolution of ego: its capacity to organize and integrate experience. Its evolution, however, takes other forms and goes in other directions as well, and with these we hope to deal in subsequent chapters.

We have sought to trace the winding but relentless course of evolution from its simplest organic beginnings to its eventuation in the psychophysical constitution of man, only then to see its continuation in the unfolding of cultural and psychological processes of increasing complexity. In response to man's neurophysiological predisposition, and the interaction of cultural with psychological processes, a specific psychological apparatus of adaptation, ego, has evolved within the personality of man.

When we contemplate any given individual in the light of his biological, genetic history—and we can do so only as a feat of imaginative thinking—we are overwhelmed by the complexity of his genetic inheritance and by the incalculable possibilities of combination and recombination of genes which made him the individual he is.* Now we must perform an even greater feat, for we must add to all this complexity the

---

* C. Judson Herrick[13] states:

"The human ovum contains forty-eight chromosomes, twenty-four from each parent. The number of different genes in these chromosomes is believed to be of the order of about thirty thousand. The genes of each parent differ from each other and are differently arranged. In fertilization the paternal chromosomes are paired with the maternal, and in this rearrangement the chance against two individuals having exactly the same pattern of combination of chromosomes is about 300,000,000,-000,000 to 1. So we see why no two people in the world (except identical twins) are exactly alike genetically, and these innate differences are accentuated by the diverse cultural influences to which they respond."

cumulative cultural history of mankind with its own evolution, which has shaped the evolving ego of our imaginary individual. Although highly individuated, he is not alone in the characteristic quality of his ego; he reflects to a certain extent a trend within his group for a given time and place in history. The sociopsychological history of ego evolution as it is the product of the interaction of culture and psychological processes plus the effects of the psychosocial climate of a given time is responsible for the trend that gives the general background coloration to the individual ego. To this conception of a phylogenetic background for ego in cultural terms must be added another dimension, which we have already described: the tendency of ego to evolve to higher levels of organization. All this we must understand about mankind before we can correctly assess the individual development of man.

▪ REFERENCES

1. Huxley, J.: *Evolution in Action.* Harper & Row, New York, 1953, pp. 8, 86, 153.
2. Magoun, H. W., Darling, L., and Prost, J.: The evolution of man's brain. In Brazier, M. A. B., Ed.: *Central Nervous System and Behavior.* Josiah Macy, Jr., Foundation, New York, 1960, pp. 33-126.
3. Clark, W. E. LeGros: *The Antecedents of Man.* Quadrangle Books, Chicago, 1960.
4. Simpson, G. G., Pittendrigh, C. S., and Tiffany, L. H.: *Life.* Harcourt, Brace, New York, 1957, pp. 212-219, 469, 741-742.
5. Mayr, E.: *Animal Species and Evolution.* Harvard University Press, Cambridge, Mass., 1963, pp. 8, 203.
6. Simpson, G. G.: The problem of plan and purpose in nature.

Sci. Monthly 1947 64:481-495 (quoted in E. Mayr, *Animal Species and Evolution*, 1963, p. 202).
7. Simpson, G. G.: *The Meaning of Evolution*. Yale University Press, New Haven, 1950, pp. 256, 258.
8. Scott, J. P.: *Animal Behavior*. University of Chicago, Chicago, 1958, pp. 100-103, 153.
9. Skinner, B. F.: Some contributions to an experimental analysis of behavior to psychology as a whole. *Am. Psychologist* 8:69-78, 1953.
10. Simpson, G. G.: The world into which Darwin led us. *Science* 1:967, 1960.
11. Young, J. Z.: *Doubt and Certainty in Science*. Clarendon Press, Oxford, 1950.
12. Tinbergen, N.: *The Study of Instinct*. Clarendon Press, Oxford, 1958, Ch. V.
13. Herrick, C. J.: *The Evolution of Human Nature*. University of Texas Press, Austin, 1956, p. 115.

4 · THE IMPRISONMENT OF TIME
AND THE WHIP OF EVOLUTION

Time, the modern physicists instruct us, is a relative concept. It has existence only in relation to some reference point or process in the universe. So it is with space, which refers merely to an arrangement of objects within it. Time and space form reference points for each other so that "what we call an hour is actually a measurement in space—an arc of 15 degrees in the apparent daily rotation of the celestial sphere."[1] We, therefore, on the planet Earth measure time in reference to movement or position in space relative to the sun. The sun is our point of reference. For other time-space relationships in the universe, there are other points of reference.

To make the conception more graphic, Einstein has pointed out that a clock whose rhythm is mechanically geared to our solar system slows down if it becomes part of another moving system which approaches the velocity of light.[1]

However, life, as we know it, is not part of another moving system outside the solar system; it is earth-bound. It has arisen out of the conditions pertaining to the relationship of earth to sun, and its time-space reference point is, therefore, fixed. The human heartbeat, the seasonal migration of birds, or the closing of a flower with the fading of the last rays of sunlight are all phenomena in tune with that part of the universe out of which they evolved, namely, our solar system.

In the course of the reciprocal relationship between the terrestrial conditions that made life possible and the living substance itself, there was laid down in the living tissue the history of this relationship in time-space terms. Organisms functioned in time not only in the sense that overt behavioral action was geared to terrestrial changes in light, temperature, season, moisture, etc., but time became an internalized aspect of their metabolism. "The time of daily activity in animals has proved so significant in their over-all adaptation to the rhythm of environmental change that many have *evolved* internal timing devices or clocks."[2] And further: "The bee also uses its internal clock to arrive in time for the opening of a flower which yesterday proved rich in nectar. The flower also uses a 'clock' to time its opening hour!"[2]

Thus, internalized biological time evolved out of the need of living things to be synchronized with the time of the solar system. Life has caught the rhythm of its terrestrial world and imprisoned it in its tissues.

It is through evolution, through the emergence of life and its further advance, that time, which is relative in the universe, came to be absolute within its own system: the system of interacting organism and environment. But evolution did not only capture time, it made it palpable in terms of its direction and its rate of acceleration.

Let us imagine that the history of life on our planet is an enormous moving picture. We are in the picture as actors; yet, we can be outside it and view it, as if some film editor had stopped the projector at our own historical point in time and given us the privilege of examining the "stills" of which we are a part, and, in addition, played back the entire film from the beginning. The "stills" would at first not surprise us too much. We would see a world with seas and continents, with mountains, plains and rivers, with a variety of climates, much like the world of our childhood geography books. There would be myriad creatures in this world, from the simplest algae in a pool of water to the most complex—ourselves. We would marvel at how well each organism is adapted to its own environment, even though we might have some misgivings about ourselves. If we were observant, we might notice that certain things resemble each other: all fish have gills; all birds have wings; a horse and a zebra are quite similar. Strange as it might seem, within the "still" everything would be in movement, responding to some aspect of the environment. But now we begin the *great* movement, the "play back," and we flash back to the beginning. As the reel unwinds, we are awe-struck and at the same time somewhat bored. The resemblance of this setting to our physical world scarcely exists. Is it a vast sea, an ill-defined cloud mass? We are not sure. But the reel turns interminably and scarcely anything happens. It turns and turns. Did we see something move in the right-hand corner of the picture? Perhaps. We summon our patience, and then we are sure. Some little living thing is there. It multiplies; there are two, and suddenly many more. Everything is moving. Perhaps there is a story, after all, perhaps it has a plot.

The earth itself changes; the action in the film is not quite so slow. Here there is land where there had been none before. A strange fishlike creature wriggles among some plants in the sea. The reel keeps turning, the picture unfolds, and more and more happens within each foot of film. We see plants on the land; there are all kinds of fish in the sea. How can we keep track of it all? How did it become so complicated? And suddenly we see the point of the story. As the earth keeps changing, so everything within it and upon it changes. Each change has some relationship to what went before; life is getting more and more complex. Its cast of characters is increasing in number and the succeeding characters are often more intricate than the preceding ones. With more characters and more complicated ones, there is more action in the story, for they are all relating to each other as well as to the physical world in which they find themselves; and there are more possibilities in the changing world for the creation of new characters out of the existing ones. The point of the story is its direction and its gathering tempo.

The turning reel is the time of our solar system; the images and action on the film are our tangible measurements of time as created by the evolution of life. Against the steady background of the reel's unwinding, for two billion years the whip of evolution has beaten out more complex forms of fitness within the framework of a changing world.

But time, measured against events, moved slowly at first. From the simplest beginnings of life until the appearance of the earliest fishes, a period well over one and a half billion years elapsed. In other words, roughly more than three-quarters of the time of our whole film story was required for the appearance of the first vertebrates. Once they appeared, however, only 260 million years passed before the first mammals evolved, and from that time approximately 170 million years were required for the emergence of man. In *Life*, Simpson, Pittendrigh, and Tiffany[2] have made an excellent graphic representation of the speeding up of the evolutionary process by plotting the temporal course of evolution on an imaginary twenty-four-hour time clock which is divided into two halves of twelve hours each, one representing the morning hours, the other, the evening ones. On such a clock, fossil remains become abundant only at 6 P.M. and man makes his appearance well after the eleventh hour, at about a quarter-second before midnight.

But what of this gathering momentum? What is being accelerated? We cannot say the hastening pace is moving toward the creation of man as an evolutionary goal. We are but part of the stream, not its end. If a stone gathers momentum as it rolls downhill, the increase in tempo is understood in relation to gravitational force. In relation to what is evolution gathering momentum? In a general way, we might say it is in relation to the increasing complexity of structure and function of organisms. But what, in the last analysis, is the increasing complexity? It is in large part an improvement in the reaction to and interaction with the environment. The living organism and its environment are an interacting system. Channels have evolved for communication between the two parts of that system. It is the evolution of these channels of communication that has an increasing tempo.

For the animal world, a most important channel, and one which is ultimately crucial to the specific character of man's adaptation, is the evolutionary development of nervous tissue which is interwoven with that of other structures and functions.

"Progressive evolution of behavior in the animal world has led to the interposing of more and more nervous processes between the stimuli arriving from the environment and the organism's responses to them."[3]

The evolution of the nervous system parallels in its tempo that of evolution as a whole. In the simplest unicellular organisms, impulses resulting from stimulation in the environment are conducted through the body as a whole, but in an organism as primitive as the jelly fish, we clearly have the appearance of a nerve net as a result of some specialization of structure. In such a system, there exist short nerve fibers and synapses with fibers of adjacent neurons; but the function is confined to the co-ordination and spreading of simple responses that involve the conduction of impulses from scattered sensory cells to effectors, i.e., muscular cells. Once this step in specialization has been made, the process of elaboration gains momentum in the direction of greater sensitivity to the environment, and more complex regulatory mechanisms in relation to it. Already in the flat worm, there are present a simple brain, two long nerves, and a network of other fibers which form the basic characteristics of all the later elaborated aspects of the nervous system. However, to reach this point in evolution took approximately six times as long as the time required for the evolution of man from the first vertebrates. There seems to exist in the oriented and directional character of evolution a *principle of improved elaboration on a theme*. Apparently, the more that *has* evolved in terms of responsiveness to the environment, the more *can* evolve subsequently—and this at gathering speed. So that we might say that especially for those organisms whose adaptation depends on a greater plasticity in relation to the environment and ultimately, as in the case of the primates, upon its control, *the rate of evolution is in large measure a function of the complexity of the organization of the nervous system.**

---

* In speaking of the genetic evolution of morphological characters, Le-Gros Clark[4] cites a line of argument, followed by E. B. Ford (The genetic basis of adaptation, In DeBeer, G. R., Ed.: *Evolution*, London, 1938, p. 43), which bears on and has its analogue in our concerns with the rate of evolution as it relates to structure.

". . . as any evolving group becomes more and more specialized in adaptation to one particular mode of life, the possible variations which could be

With the evolution of man, there evolved, as a result of the interaction of his high degree of intelligence with other structural changes, a new mechanism: the capacity to create culture. Man could consciously regulate his environment and himself in it through the creation of artifacts, language, social structure, varying economies, etc. If we think that the tempo of evolution had been gathering momentum up to the advent of man, then this increase in tempo is nothing compared to the rate of cultural evolution. The appearance of the first hominids goes back about one million years; modern man in the evolutionary sense, i.e., Stone Age man, about fifty thousand, and historical man only five or six thousand years. Within the historical period, the age of technology is little over a hundred years old, and the atomic age is an event of our own lifetime—a matter of twenty to forty years. As Loren Eiseley[5] has put it: "Never before in history has it been literally possible to have been born in one age and to die in another."

But culture is only the external manifestation of a process that must originate within man himself, and that must have an evolution of its own.

What of the actor who stepped out of the film? A process must have been gathering momentum within him that finally led to the emergence of consciousness, to the experience of awareness. And with it, he knew time. It was "his own time," at first very primitive: the awareness of his life span, of the interval between childhood and maturity; of the time of gestation; of the growth of his young, and the death of his

---

of use to it become progressively restricted. 'Finally,' he goes on to say, 'it attains a state of "orthogenesis" in which the only changes open to the species are those which push it along the path it has already pursued.' It need hardly be said that in using the term 'orthogenesis' Ford is not referring here to the effects of an inherent tendency within the organism to evolve in a certain direction, but to the effects of what has been called 'orthoselection.' "

predecessors. He experienced time in relation to the events of his daily life and to his position in space. It took a certain time to track down his prey or to cover a certain distance to a given shelter. There was time in relation to the products of his work. How long did it take to make an ax, or to skin an animal? Perhaps, he noticed that his primitive tool inventions saved him some time. Gradually, as awareness was sharpened, more subjective aspects of the time experience evolved. There were wishes and needs whose fulfillment must be postponed. A future was created, and the feeling about the passage of time varied with differing emotional situations.

All these time experiences had to be integrated; the various awarenesses had to be synchronized. Time was no longer completely imprisoned within his tissues so that, like the bee, he knew automatically when to come to the open flower; it had become part of his awareness, and his function in time and space was governed by that structure which had evolved in order to integrate his experiences: his ego. As his culture and psychological life grew in complexity, so also did his ego, since the regulatory mechanism had to be adequate to its task. Ego kept time for man, but it was a delicate and intricate clock: sometimes in tune with nature's imprisoned time, some of which he still held in his tissues; sometimes upset by it but always striving for harmony and stability;[6] and yet always changing.

Ego is part of that great movement of life which we visualized in the unwinding film reel, and it appears at a time in the moving picture story when things are happening rapidly. In fact, it is a most important factor in making things happen, at gathering tempo. It expands the areas of function and awareness for man, and, having done so, it must itself expand in order to integrate what it has created. It is the timekeeper and the whip of man's evolution.

✷ REFERENCES

1. Barnett, L.: *The Universe and Dr. Einstein*. Mentor, New York, 1950, pp. 51, 61.
2. Simpson, G. G., Pittendrigh, C. S., and Tiffany, L. H.: *Life*. Harcourt, Brace, New York, 1957, pp. 208, 735.
3. Dobzhansky, T.: *Mankind Evolving*. Yale University Press, New Haven, 1962, p. 203.
4. Clark, W. E. LeGros: *The Fossil Evidence for Human Evolution*. University of Chicago Press, Chicago, 1955, p. 42.
5. Eiseley, L.: *The Firmament of Time*. Atheneum, New York, 1960, p. 133.
6. Cannon, W. B.: *The Wisdom of the Body*. W. W. Norton, New York, 1932.

5 ▪ THE EXCEPTIONAL INDIVIDUAL

We have attempted thus far to differentiate man's psychological evolution from his biological and cultural evolution, at the same time recognizing the close interrelationship and interaction among these aspects of the evolutionary process. By psychological evolution we refer to the evolution of ego functions, i.e., to an advance, for example, in the degree of perceptiveness, intelligence, capacity to integrate, achieve autonomy, interact socially, love, and to create cultural products, among them value systems. These capacities have been evolving since the emergence of man, and we will deal with certain aspects of this evolution in greater detail below. At this point, however, we should like to concern ourselves with the problem of how such evolution operates, what sparks it, and what is the vehicle for its transmission.

In all species, despite common characteristics which enable us to classify them as a unit, there are differences among individuals. These differences are greater in number, degree, and variety the higher the organism stands in the evolutionary hierarchy, i.e., the greater the complexity of structured function. This is a simple fact of probability resulting from the operation of the genetic mechanisms by which traits are transmitted from generation to generation. The greater the number of traits—or, in other words, the more information the genetic material carries—the more opportunity for a variety of recombinations. In an organism as complex as man, the number of hereditary recombinations would seem to be almost infinite, and the result is a degree of individuation unknown in other species.[1] It is this individuation which is crucial for psychological as well as cultural evolution.

Let us envisage the situation of prehistoric man—of Stone Age man, for example. Our anthropological textbooks tell us in a general way that in that period man discovered the use of tools, he learned how to chip flints, to make a sharp point, or a cutting edge, to make an ax with a handle, to master the use of fire. But only in the imaginative, poetic works of a writer like J. V. Jensen[2] or in Greek mythology do we find an attempt to reconstruct how this actually happened. It must have happened through the inventiveness of one individual, or a number of them, whose inherent capacities stood out above those of others. The discoverer of fire—and indeed there were probably many discoverers—must have been more vital, more enterprising, and therefore more courageous and imaginative than his fellows. The inventor of the first tools must likewise have had superior intelligence. Such native endowments in given individuals must have come to fruition within a specific, felicitous framework of circumstances that provided for their realization.

The biological evolution of man in a general sense has provided him with the organic equipment which made possible his subsequent cultural and psychological evolution, but it is through the emergence of exceptional individuals that such evolution is implemented and set into operation. Such exceptional individuals can be likened to genetic mutants in a given species population. If the mutations serve the survival needs of the population, they will be selected out in the interaction of organisms and environment, and a biological evolutionary step will have been made. In a similar way, although by no means always so directly or immediately, the cultural contribution of exceptional individuals, to the extent that they serve the survival and advance of the culture, will remain as landmarks that have influenced the evolutionary development of the culture.

All such advances are predicated on the fact that man is a social being. His actual physical survival depends on some sort of familial form and some organization of his means of subsistence. These social organizations are manifestations of his capacity for culture and are in themselves evolving. We are confronted in the case of man not with a linear, causally determined evolutionary process, but with an intricate patterning of forces and factors, some organic, some cultural, and some psychological, which interact with each other.

Washburn,[2] for example, has advanced the theory that it is not only man's opposable thumb and his great intelligence which made possible the discovery of tools, but that this discovery in itself, as an aspect of culture, served to create selection pressure for those individuals with greater "handedness" and greater intelligence. A trait which has evolved on the basis of organic evolution, through its influence on culture creates a new environment in which selection again operates in an evolutionary direction.

So it must also be with man's social structures. These evolved, as we have said, for survival reasons, but their evolution was made possible by man's capacity to learn and by his need and ability to communicate what he has learned.

The capacity to learn, remember, and in some form conceptualize, i.e., symbolize, is specifically human, although it is based, like the evolution of all living things, in the biological. The characteristically human aspects of learning, consciousness and symbolic representation, together with communication through language, have created the basis not only for culture but for what we choose to call psychological evolution. Man did not merely invent tools; he *experienced* their invention. He thought about the problems involved in the making of an ax head: about the selection of materials, the best ways of chipping at the stone, the form to be created in relation to the function to be served. He experienced disappointment, frustration, perhaps rage when he encountered recalcitrant materials, when he was unable to solve the problems posed by his first glimmering of a creative idea. And he enjoyed his success when he made a good and useful tool. His success, in turn, had far-reaching effects on his actual physical survival as well as on his social situation.

But more important, the experience of invention extended his sphere of ego function. Not only did the tool make possible the exercise of new functions, but also the act and experience of inventing and making it enlarged an entire range of ego experiences—experiences that have to do with perception, discrimination, problem solving, manual skill, emotional responses, feelings about the self. This expansion of psychological experience, integrated as it is by the functioning ego, represents an evolutionary advance in psychological terms.

It has as its prerequisite organic, genetic evolution. It interacts continuously with, and rebounds to influence the course of, cultural evolution. But it is in constant movement, for every extension of psychological experience provides new opportunities for a further expansion of such experience, and thus for cultural change.*

The exceptional individual is one whose native endowments have enabled him to evolve psychologically beyond the general level of his group; but for the products of such psychological evolution to affect the culture as a whole, they must in some way be transmitted or communicated. Language, and much later written language, are, of course, the most obvious ways of communication, although artifacts, paintings, social structures also speak for and transmit the creations of the past. Although in historical times we are aware of the tremendous influence of single individuals on cultural evolution and on its psychological concomitants, we can scarcely imagine that the fundamental evolutionary steps of early man are attributable to single individuals. Yet, we have spoken of the exceptional individual and his role as a mutant in his cultural situation. Let us clarify the point.

Whenever we consider evolution, whether biological, cultural, or psychological, we must think in terms of entire populations. To be regarded as evolutionary, changes which take place must, in biological terms, produce long-term improvement in relation to environmental conditions; must, in cultural terms, produce a new and advanced culture; and must, in psychological terms, produce advanced ways in which the mind of man deals with himself, his fellows, and

---

* Since we are concerned here with the general way in which psychological evolution operates, we will not deal at this point with the problem of the negative influences of certain psychological experiences either ontogenetically or in terms of their influence on a given cultural situation. Certainly, psychological as well as sociocultural evolution has by-paths which do not invariably lead in the direction of advance.

his physical environment. Processes that effect such broad changes are bound to be slow and cumulative, and require the involvement of many individuals within a total population to produce a new form. In terms of psychobiological endowment, one might envisage a hierarchy of exceptional individuals, the most advanced of whom function as catalysts to stimulate in others a receptivity to and assimilation of whatever new and advanced cultural contributions they have made.* A process of diffusion takes place within a culture,

---

* After this chapter had been written and at the time of the completion of the entire manuscript, Margaret Mead's book, *Continuities in Cultural Evolution*,⁴ was published. She considers the unit of change in what she terms cultural microevolution to be the unique individual, surrounded by a group or "cluster" of significant individuals who are able to reinforce and help disseminate throughout a population the particular cultural contribution or invention of the "leader."

An excellent and very moving illustration of this process is described in Chapter IX, "The Paliau Movement." The Manus peoples of the Admiralty Islands were transformed from the most primitive culture into the crude beginnings of a modern social organization by the interaction of opportunities for evolutionary advance created by the contact with Western society (the American Army during World War II) and the imagination of a gifted leader, Paliau. These factors flourished in the fertile soil of the malcontent of the Manus peoples with good reason: They were poor, had poor land and few resources, there were no prospects for appreciable improvement, and they were ripe for change. Paliau, directly or indirectly inspired by the spectacle of American egalitarianism and the high level of technology and social organization, was able to organize local leaders around him and to propose the carrying out of a social program which called for (1) a widening of the sphere of human sympathy and a diminution therefore of near-neighbor antagonisms; (2) an almost complete giving up of old traditions; (3) long-time planning and saving for the future in order to build a new way of life.

What emerges from this example is not only the manner in which a single gifted individual, given the opportune time and place, can change the cultural level of a group, as Dr. Mead indicates, but also the implicit psychological change that must accompany such cultural change. There are new attitudes toward others, new feelings of self-respect, new feelings of mastery and efficacy, new attitudes toward time. For these inner changes, Paliau is himself the model, for he has shown his people advanced social, ethical, and aesthetic levels of behavior.

therefore, in the course of which the general population absorbs, through learning, the new forms that have been introduced by exceptional individuals. The accretion over long periods of time of new forms in many areas, e.g., areas of physical artifacts, social forms, new knowledge and ideas, ultimately leads to the creation of a new culture.

Let us remember that these cultural advances, while they take place on a nongenetic basis, are predicated on man's biological evolution as expressed in the general, phylogenetic advance of the species and ever-increasing individuation. In turn, man's psychological evolution is predicated on his cultural advance, although here the two processes are so intertwined that one can scarcely distinguish cause and effect. For example, at some early point in man's development, his survival depended on the hunting of large game. This enterprise called for not only the invention of weapons, but also the co-operation of many men. The need to co-operate inevitably produced new psychological attitudes: greater interaction and communication among individuals, certain kinds of dependency, esteem and affection; differences in role and status among individuals; competitive feelings; feelings of security in belonging to a group. These effects, however, are not merely new; they are evolutionary in character, because they represent an expansion of psychological functioning and a creation of opportunities for still further expansions. Thus, every evolutionary step in culture creates new opportunities for psychological evolution, which in turn further influences cultural, as well as psychological, advance. We cannot leave the subject of the exceptional individual, his role as catalyst in cultural and psychological advance, and the manner of the transmission of his contribution, without making two important points. Many individuals can be "exceptional" in various ways, and this not always through their tangible contributions. An especially loving mother, by providing a growing child with an optimal opportunity for the autonomous and fullest development of his ego, can make an important contribution to societal evolution and to the possibility of higher levels of ego function for future generations. Furthermore, the transmission of such contributions does not take place through processes of conscious learning alone but through unconscious identifications, a theme with which we will deal in a subsequent chapter.

Measured against the slow pace of biological evolution, the evolution of the culture and psychology of man has proceeded at a rapid rate. Each progressive elaboration of a culture form produces such extensive elaborations and differentiations of psychic functioning which extend beyond the cultural advance, that they result in ever new and greater opportunities for the evolutionary contributions of exceptional individuals. These contributions in turn become focal points for further advances, with a resultant heaping up of environmental niches, in the cultural and psychological sense, to be filled by individuals from the total population.

▪ REFERENCES

1. Medawar, P. B.: *The Uniqueness of the Individual*. Basic Books, New York, 1961.
2. Jensen, J. V.: *The Long Journey*. Knopf, New York, 1945.
3. Washburn, S. L.: Speculations on the interrelations of the history of tools and biological evolution. In Spuhler, J. N., Ed., *The Evolution of Man's Capacity for Culture*. Wayne State University Press, Detroit, 1959, pp. 21-31.
4. Mead, M.: *Continuities in Cultural Evolution*. Yale University Press, New Haven, 1964.

6 · WHAT IS PSYCHOLOGICAL EVOLUTION?

IT IS OFTEN the custom when viewing the history of civilization in large perspective to refer to certain epochs in general,
ized, inclusive terms. So, for example, we speak of the Golden
Age of Pericles, the Dark Ages, the Renaissance, the Age of
Enlightenment, the Age of Reason, or the era of Industrial
Revolution. What do we hope to convey by these names?
They refer to Western man's prevailing way of viewing
life, the world, and himself: Through their use, we acknowledge that an era in human development has its own specific
character.

The ethos of a period in history or of a people in a given
space-time dimension is not a material product of culture in

the sense that artifacts, art forms, or even societal organization is palpable. Rather it is testimony of *inner psychological processes* which reflect on the nature of material objects created within a culture, whose influence then in turn rebounds on the specific nature of these inner processes.

Thus, the existence of a particular coloration in the mode of a culture suggests that psychological processes of a collective nature are at work. There is a common psychological denominator within a population responsible for the emergence of its ethos. So, for example, Edith Hamilton,[1] in speaking of Greece, writes: "That which distinguishes the modern world from the ancient, and that which divides the West from the East is the supremacy of mind in the affairs of men, and this came to birth in Greece and lived in Greece alone of all the ancient world. The Greeks were the first intellectualists. In a world where the irrational had played the chief role, they came forward as the protagonists of the mind."

The importance of this characterization is that in dealing with a people's way of functioning in and relating to the world, a psychological dimension is introduced by which change is observable. It is our contention that such change, for which the naming of historical epochs is but a loosely conceived illustration, reflects an evolutionary process in psychological terms. Such a process is an aspect of sociocultural evolution, in the sense that it is nonorganic, although grounded in the neurophysiological acquisitions of man. In the products—both material and non-material—which it creates at different times and among different peoples and by which we deduce the nature of inner states responsible for such creations, psychological evolution represents not only diversification but a general, although by no means consistent or unilinear, advance.

Hallowell,[2] the anthropologist whose writings evince a keen appreciation of the evolutionary dimension in the development of man, asks the important question: ". . . what is the emergence of a cultural mode of adaptation a function of?" He concludes that a concern with man's psychological evolution is an essential prerequisite of a satisfactory answer to this question. In the gregarious nature of the primates and in the potentiality thus created for socialization, he sees man's link with his anthropoid ancestors. The crucial point of evolutionary differentiation, however, resides in man's capacity to develop a generic, psychic structure. This results from the ability to internalize the perceptual world in terms of symbols and to communicate these within the framework of a social group. "The achievement of a human status in the evolutionary process, when taken inclusively, is not to be conceived as a simple function of the possession of specific organic traits—brain size, foot structure, or some specific psychological traits such as intelligence—but as a total *psychobiological* adjustment that implies an overlaid psychological structure functionally integrated with organic structure."[2]

The introduction of the concept of an inner psychological structuring of personality, arising out of and functioning in a social medium, as an important aspect of human evolution bridges the gap between organic and cultural evolution. Hallowell looks to psychoanalysis for the model of this structure, making the point that in the phylogenetic understanding of man we owe to the observations of psychoanalysis the realization "that universal dynamic processes are involved which are related to the psychobiological nature of modern man as a species." He further states: "One of the seminal contributions of the psychoanalysts . . . was to hypothecate a model of personality organization, conceptualized in 'structural terms.' . . . In phylogenetic perspective, the psychoanalytic model of personality structure suggests that one of the things we must account for in human evolution is not simply a 'human mind' in the abstract, but a generic type of personality organization which did not exist, perhaps at the earliest hominid level."[3] Within the personality organization herein referred to, it is the human ego which to our mind is crucial to psychological evolution. We use the term "ego" in its broadest, phylogenetic sense as defined in Chapter III, viewing it as process as well as structure, and including super-ego and ego ideal functions as differentiated aspects of its entirety. Hallowell's evolutionary point of view is an important contribution in that it brings into relief a point of demarcation: that point between those hominids who lacked personality organization as we understand it today and modern man in the sense of *Homo sapiens*. In other words, it posits an evolutionary step for personality organization and therefore, in our terms, a point at which ego had evolved.

Ego, however, does not merely exist, having evolved out of some lesser form of nervous organization; it continues to function in the most active interplay conceivable with environment, both physical and cultural. Its nature, therefore, is not only determined by this interaction in the sense of a striving toward adjustment, but by the tendencies of all manifestations of life to evolve—to seek out opportunities for development toward higher and more complex levels of organization, and in the case of ego in relationship to culture, to create these opportunities.

If one views only the *products* of ego throughout the history of culture—artifacts, system of economy, social structure, art, beliefs, and traditions of a given society—one arrives, it is true, at some hierarchical picture of culture which is evolutionary, but one's conception of ego itself remains fairly static. One is impressed then by the fact that, as Wissler[3, 4] expressed it, "there were constant and recurrent categories of culture that transcended any particular mode of cultural adaptation," and that this universal pattern exists because of the "common nature of man and certain invariant properties in the human situation." The fact of ego is one of these invariant properties, but its *nature*, as expressed in the extent of its grasp of reality, in its characteristic way of relating to others, its world conception, the extent of its sensitivity and responsiveness to stimuli, its ethical level, and the extent of its self-awareness and self-realization, has been evolving since its inception under the pressure of culture and history which it at once creates and by which its own varying and evolving forms are created. It is the common denominator in the *nature* of ego within a population circumscribed by a particular time-space dimension that is one important factor in determining how we describe an epoch in human sociocultural evolution.

The particular contribution of psychotherapy to the understanding of the evolutionary dimension in personality is made possible through observations in numerous cases of what might be called the "dynamic ego." We refer here not primarily to ego in its psychodynamic interaction with other parts of the personality, or of its developmental history in the life of the individual, as these are usually understood in psychoanalysis. Rather, we are concerned with the observation within a situation frankly committed to change, of the advance of the individual ego, not solely in that it seeks adjustment, but rather a higher degree of complexity, integration, and self-realization. This becomes apparent in the psychotherapeutic situation because we see the individual in historical perspective, i.e., we can assess the character of his ego, of which his strivings are a part, in relation to that of his antecedents. Furthermore, we observe the functioning of his ego within a cultural framework. We see what new integrative tasks have been posed by the environment—tasks which are often responsible for his having sought out psychotherapy. In his interaction with his social environment, we are able to assess how he uses the evolutionary opportunities

which it presents and in what ways his own activity contributes to the expansion of these opportunities for the culture
as a whole.

Our view of psychological evolution is inevitably sharpened by observing ego function within a societal framework
that offers many opportunities for cultural, social, and psychological expansion. A society which is relatively young and
unbound by tradition, or one which represents the interaction of many varying traditions and customs, functioning
to build a social unit within a vast geographic domain, provides new psychological as well as physical frontiers. The
United States is an example of such a society. Waddington[5]
appreciates fully the cultural evolutionary processes which
take place here. "Where cultural changes have occurred, however, as in the Manus, or the immigrant population in the
United States, the real importance of the evolutionary altera-
tions is unquestionable." In the opening up of a new continent,
a great niche was created for the survival needs of large segments of the European population. Sometimes these needs
existed almost exclusively in terms of physical survival, and
the new land represented economic, vocational, educational,
and social opportunities. In other cases, the new continent
provided religious or political asylum for the free expression
of what were regarded, in the old cultural framework, as
heretical ideas. The meeting of such needs was as essential to
human survival and evolution in the psychological sense as
was the greater chance of economic survival.

The historical events which gave rise to this open-ended
society based on a conception of individual freedom and
expansion created a valuable area of observation for the
psychologist, especially for the psychotherapist. Within a
single cultural framework, two psychologically divergent
generations were juxtaposed: one rooted preponderantly in
the traditions, mores, and ego mode of its country of origin,

yet not wishing to impose these fully upon the succeeding generation because of a conscious desire to provide opportunities for their children which they themselves lacked; the other, responding to the environmental opportunities for new ways, yet in conflict about loyalty to parental values. It is this second generation which constitutes a large portion of the psychotherapist's patient population.* In the therapeutic situation, under the pressure of conflict (particularly sharpened by our societal framework) between parental modes and the autonomous strivings of ego, the ego's attempt to achieve higher, more differentiated degrees of integration is observable. This is the struggle to reconcile opposing internalized and largely unconscious attitudes regarding authority, the right to self-autonomy, and the nature of relationship to others, and to emerge with an advance in ego organization. We may justifiably assume that a society which respects and encourages individuation,† which makes available to a greater segment of the population the accumulated experience of its culture and offers to more individuals the opportunity for the fulfillment of their potentialities in action, is one which furnishes fertile soil for the further evolution of ego.

In numerous cases which come to our attention in psychotherapy, "the push for a better life that comes from within a person," as one patient put it, makes itself manifest. The most obvious form which this striving takes is in the vocational life of an individual. It is not uncommon in the United States for the son of a tailor to become an important scientist; or that

---

* Although it is often literally the second generation that is most conflicted, the term "second generation" can also be construed metaphorically to express a psychological attitude, since with the passage of time the second generation has become in reality the third or fourth generation.

† So much has been expressed in current literature concerning the American need for conformity that it may seem paradoxical to speak of a respect for individuation. Yet, precisely these contradictory forces exist side by side in American life.

of a small shopkeeper, a politically significant figure; or that of an artisan, an outstanding social scientist. The advance from the immigrant generation to the succeeding one in the work life of individuals is exemplified on all sides. This does not mean merely a different type of activity, nor a better way of earning a living, or of achieving greater economic security, although these may all be aspects of such change. In many cases, they may even represent the limits of change. Nevertheless, from the standpoint of psychosocial evolution and of inner psychological advance, the vocational improvement represents a closer approximation to the fulfillment of ego potentialities and inevitably places the individual within a niche that expands his sphere of positive influence over a larger segment of the population. In this way, his vocational advance may become one important vehicle for the dissemination not only of technological or scientific advances, but also of ethical advances, equalitarian ideas, and higher levels of human relatedness.

The evolutionary level of an individual ego will rarely represent advance in all the categories which we have mentioned as criteria; in fact, in certain categories there may be no advance at all, or even retrogression. But, that such advances as exist are communicated through vocational, educational, or social interaction within a fluid societal environment makes them evolutionarily operative.

It is worth noting that the manifestations of psychological evolution as we observe them through higher levels of ego organization are not inevitably psychological or psychiatric casualties of the sociocultural evolutionary process. We observe them in our patients simply because this is *our* field of observation: a field in which such processes which exist throughout our society are brought into particularly sharp relief.

Certain authors, notably E. Erikson, in their concern

with the ego in relation to historical and sociocultural processes have tended to emphasize the importance of such concepts as *harmony* of the ego-identity with the historical
situation, or *perpetuation of tradition* through psychosocial
processes. In order to differentiate our own concepts from
theirs, let us return momentarily to certain conceptions which
characterize evolution biologically. One of the most important early advances in organic evolution was the storing
of information in the genetic material and the reduction in
mutation rate. This guaranteed, from the standpoint of reproduction, the perpetuation in consistent form of a given species.
Evolution, which followed this early advance, however,
depended on the appearance of variants within this consist-
ency and on the operation of selection pressure on these as
described above. We have, therefore, a principle of stability
and a principle of change within the evolutionary process.
The principle of stability ensures continuity; the principle of
change ensures advance.

These two aspects of evolution are manifest in man's
cultural and psychosocial evolution as well. Were it not so
there would be, in terms of the principle of stability, no
clearly delineated units of culture, and no continuity of
sociocultural forms and of corresponding levels of psychological evolution: On the other hand, in terms of the principle
of change, there would be no advancing continuum of cultural and psychological evolution.

When Erikson[6] writes: "The growing child must derive a
vitalizing sense of reality from the awareness that his individual way of mastering experience (his ego synthesis) is a
successful variant of a group identity and is *in accord* with
its space-time and life plan," or later, in speaking of the
"incestuous" choice of a mate "who resembles infantile love
objects," when he says, "Such a choice follows an ethnic
mechanism in that it creates a continuity between the family

one grew up in and the family one establishes: it thus perpet-
uates tradition, i.e., the sum of all that had been learned by
preceding generations, in analogy to the *preservation of the
gains of evolution* in the mating within the species," the
emphasis is on the conservative aspect of evolution, rather
than on its forward movement as well. For psychological
and sociocultural evolution to take place, for there to be any
"gains" which can then be consolidated into socially usable
and transmissible form, the individual ego, or at least the egos
of a sufficient number of individuals within a culture, must
advance *beyond* what could be regarded as a *"successful
variant"* within the group to a higher degree of individuation,
thus forming foci from which the diffusion of higher levels
of organization into the group as a whole can take place. It
is through such advances in the psychological evolution of
ego that new traditions are created, which in turn provide
new niches, new opportunities within a given culture for the
evolutionary advance of a greater number of individuals.

The parallel between this cultural, psychological interaction in the name of evolution and organic evolution is quite
evident. Through the operation of natural selection, new
environmental pressures can bring about the evolution of new
structures. Such new structures in turn provide a new environment to which the response is further evolutionary
change. The interrelationship between the evolution of man's
brain and his handedness provides such an example.[7-11] As we
know, man's brain, against the background of other essential
evolutionary steps, evolved far beyond that of other primates.
It evolved to a point at which the opposable thumb could be
implemented in the use of, and finally in the creation of, tools.
The existence of tools, the establishment of the necessary
motor-visual control for their use and creation, plus what we
may deduce about man's satisfaction in their use, created in

a summative way a new niche which greatly stimulated the further development of brain and nervous system. The further evolution of the brain, in turn, did not only improve man's handedness, which in itself would have created still further niches, but through its capacity for mastering an ever larger segment of reality must have provided many new niches to be filled by further organic, cultural, and psychological changes and improvements.* Thus, the evolution of a new form does not merely fill an existing niche, but increases through its own greater complexity, in combination with other evolved forms, the number of statistical probabilities for the creation of new niches to be filled by new, advanced evolutionary forms. Once the brain and nervous system of man had evolved, the dynamic aspect of evolution in which potentialities are progressively piling up becomes clear, not only biologically, but as it is reflected in cultural and psychological evolution. The unit of this psychological evolution is the human ego.

---

* We are aware that psychological change and improvement, as well as biological and cultural advance, do not follow a unilinear progression either in the population as a whole or in the development of individuals. Evolutionary advances in one area often play a role in so-called retrogressive manifestations in another. This is particularly true in the case of individuals, when evolutionary pressure coming either from the culture, from ego strivings, or from an interaction of both can result in neurotic personality formations. Sometimes, these are well-encapsulated and do not interfere with the general forward movement of the ego of the individual; sometimes, they pervade the personality and prevent its further development. We will deal with questions of neurosis and of psychotherapy in relation to the viewpoint of psychological evolution at a later point.

▪ **REFERENCES**

1. Hamilton, E.: *The Greek Way*. W. W. Norton, New York, 1942, p. 20.
2. Hallowell, A. I.: Personality structure and the evolution of man. *American Anthropologist* 52:164, 1950.
3. Hallowell, A. I.: Self, society and culture in phylogenetic perspective. In Tax, S., Ed.: *The Evolution of Man, Evolution After Darwin*, Vol. II. University of Chicago Press, Chicago, 1960, pp. 315; 326-327.
4. Wissler, C.: *Man and Culture*. New York, 1923, pp. 264-265. (Quoted in Hallowell,³ pp. 326-327.)
5. Waddington, C. H.: *The Ethical Animal*. Atheneum, New York, 1961, pp. 110-111.
6. Erikson, E. H.: *Identity and the Life Cycle*. Psychological Issues, Vol. I, No. 1, Monograph 1, 1959. International Universities Press, New York, p. 22.
7. Washburn, S. L.: Tools and evolution. In Spuhler, J. N., Ed.: *The Evolution of Man's Capacity for Culture*. Wayne State University Press, Detroit, 1959, pp. 28-29.
8. Clark, W. E. LeGros: *The Antecedents of Man*. Quadrangle Books, Chicago, 1960, pp. 228-265, 278, 343-349.
9. Clark, W. E. LeGros: *The Fossil Evidence for Human Evolution*. University of Chicago Press, Chicago, 1955.
10. Berrill, N. J.: *Man's Emerging Mind*. Dodd, Mead & Co., New York, 1955, pp. 77-89.
11. Magoun, H. W., Darling, L., and Prost, J.: The evolution of man's brain. In Brazier, M. A. B., Ed.: *The Central Nervous System and Behavior*. Josiah Macy, Jr., Foundation, New York, 1960, p. 42.

7 ▪ THE EGO-GENETIC IMPERATIVE

To UNDERSTAND EGO and its evolution, it is necessary first to understand the emergence of consciousness in the evolutionary process. Consciousness, the quality of organized awareness, depends on and parallels the ever greater elaboration of neurophysiological structures and functions that finally eventuate in the central nervous system of man.* This increasing complexity of organic structure results at some point in

---

* "Thus the progressive elaboration and differentiation of the cortex in the evolving Primates has led to increasing powers of apprehending the nature of external stimuli, a greater capacity for a wider range of adjustments to any environmental change, and an enhancement of the neural mechanisms for effecting more delicately co-ordinated reactions." (From Clark, W. E. LeGros')

a change from the quantitative to the qualitative; we cannot account for this new quality, consciousness, in terms of a summation of structures and their corresponding physiological functions. These summations, increased brain size, increased corticalization, increased complexity in the interaction of the hypothalamus and reticular systems, to cite only a few examples, are essential prerequisites for the advent of consciousness, but they do not explain it.

C. Judson Herrick[2] states this very aptly: "Awareness cannot be 'reduced' to physiochemical categories or adequately described scientifically by ever so complete an explanation of the mechanism employed. This is as impractical as it would be to try to describe the properties of an electric current in terms of those of the dynamo that generates it." The shift from the quantitative to the qualitative in the emergence of consciousness is the shift from the material to the mental: a transition that is as elusive as the evolutionary shift from the nonliving to the living. Yet, these evolutionary processes *have* taken place. That they are analogous, i.e., that the spectacle of evolution furnishes us not only with examples of a hierarchy of increasing complexity, but, at various points, with the emergence of new qualities—the vital from the inorganic, the mental from the purely neural—leads us to the conclusion that they represent stages in one continuous evolutionary process. This fact is extremely important to remember when we come to consider the evolution of psychic processes and organizations.

A study of the evolution of life confronts us with two aspects or principles governing the evolutionary process. One is implied in the fact of continuity, in the relatedness of organisms to one another, and therefore in the stability of certain common denominators characteristic of all life; the other is the principle of change and advance, which accounts for the great variety of forms in nature and which is exemplified in the fact of mutational change. In considering the emergence of consciousness, we must give credence to both principles: "All the evidence in the field of comparative psychology seems to point toward the presence in many infra-human animals of a simple, sensori-motor, affective and cognitive awareness of what is going on which has its expression in reinforcement, inhibition and directive guidance of behavior. These patterns of behavior and the primitive type of awareness probably colligated with them may be present in all animals; and they are progressively elaborated in forms that are recognizably similar to human mental processes, in animals which possess more or less well differentiated cerebral cortex. It seems probable, therefore, that although awareness is an emergent in the evolutionary series, it did not appear as a sudden mutation, but was gradually individuated from some more generalized type of integrated experience. All that we know about psychogenesis in the human infant points in the same direction."[2] Here, Herrick gives weight to both aspects of the evolutionary process, although the greater emphasis is on its continuity. In the emergence of consciousness as we know it in man, however, there has been added to the fact of awareness, the reflexive factor: i.e., man experiences his awareness; he knows that he is conscious. *And it is at this point that the gradual elaboration of awareness in the animal world yields to an evolutionary leap in the form of human consciousness.* The preparations for the leap had to be made in the form of the gradual accretion of neurophysiological change, but the leap itself is comparable to a sudden mutation and exemplifies the shift from quantitative to qualitative change of which we spoke earlier.*

---

* An example of the accretion of neurophysiological change and its implication for evolution is given in the following observations of LeGros Clark:[1]

"The rapid development of the temporal lobe is another distinctive char-

The clearest intimations of this change begin with the subhuman primates. Evidence indicates that monkeys, and certainly the anthropoid apes, have achieved a degree of consciousness closest to human awareness. Although not possessing language, they are able to learn and think in symbolic terms. Learning is predicated on the evolution of memory, which in simple neurophysiological terms has very early beginnings in the evolutionary sense. Thinking, and especially thinking in symbolic terms (and perhaps we cannot really speak of thinking until this level has been reached), involves the making of choices in behavioral action. For the existence of such choices in the lives of subhuman primates there is ample evidence.[3] But we would doubt that there is reflexive awareness of this making of choices, or long periods of preparatory thinking which are characteristic of human consciousness. Awareness of this high order involves the evolution of an intricate form of symbolic thinking, imagery, language, and memory. Once these requirements have been met, as indeed they have in the course of the evolutionary development of the human species, the requisite predisposition for the emergence of ego is given.

Before we leave the subject of the appearance and evolutionary development of consciousness as the precondition of the advent of ego, there are two important points we should like to make: first, that consciousness is predicated

---

acter of the Primate brain. . . . The significance of this expansion of the temporal lobe is not clear, but there is evidence of a clinical nature that . . . it constitutes a mechanism for the storage of visual memories. If this is so, its progressive development *pari passu* with the increasing elaboration of the visual powers in Primates, becomes readily intelligible, for it enhances the ability to profit from experience on the basis of visual cues. . . . Anatomically, there is also evidence that the temporal lobe receives impulses relayed, directly or indirectly, from almost all other areas of the cortex; in other words, it appears to provide the means for the final integration of the resultants of activity of the cortex as a whole."

on experience, rather than a necessary prerequisite for experience. To quote Whitehead:[4] "The principle I am adopting is that consciousness pre-supposes experience, and not experience consciousness." From the standpoint of evolutionary advance, the relationship of experience to consciousness is like that of the opposable thumb to cephalization. The evolution of the opposable thumb made possible the use of tools, for which, of course, a certain level of brain development was required. However, once this was achieved, the continuing use of tools created a new environment in which selection pressure operated in the direction of an increase in brain size.[5] One given evolutionary step calls for another. In just this way, the evolution of the increased capacity for number and variety of experience called for the evolution of consciousness.

The potential for the emergence of consciousness was reinforced by a second factor of far-reaching importance, the presence of individuation very early in the evolutionary hierarchy. For although the innate behavior patterns of animals other than man are species-characteristic and set in terms of their broad outlines, just as are morphological structures, the details of any given action in time and space are determined by the special situation and by the extent of the available plasticity in the individual organism for dealing with the situation. In general, plasticity for species has evolved as organisms have evolved in an increasing hierarchy of complexity and adaptability, but within a species there must exist individual variations in plasticity. "The completed nest, the spider's web, the act of mating, is attained by a train of acts different in detail on every occasion."[6] In some sense, the pressure or tension created in the individual by the requirements of the special situation, as these call for choices and variants in behavior above and beyond the behavior laid down in the innate, patterned response, must result in the rudiments of awareness that have eventuated in the emergence of consciousness.

Thus, the increasing capacity for experience and the *increasing potential for individuation* are potent factors in the ultimate evolution of consciousness.

We have already referred to one aspect of man's consciousness, its reflexive nature, that differentiates it from that of other creatures. This points the way to a further differentiation which we should like to make, and upon which the theme of this volume rests: namely, a differentiation between consciousness and ego. The latter could not exist without the former; yet they are not identical. In an organism as complex as man, in whom the automatic nature of behavior and experience has been in large measure replaced by its conscious control, and in whom memory and learning are of primary importance in the processes of adaptation to the environment, it would be difficult to imagine how the great variety of experiences, the multitude of sensory perceptions, the awareness of many affective states, the awareness of retrospective, introspective, and prospective thinking processes, all of which are aspects of consciousness, could serve the survival needs of the organism without some regulatory psychic apparatus. The many awarenesses which constitute human consciousness would have to be organized and integrated for their effective functioning. To this end, what we have called ego *had* to evolve.*

---

* Sir Charles Sherrington[7] has expressed a similar thought: "The mental 'now' is a unity, because whatever its items they conform to one significant pattern, a serial 'now.' To think of time as unifying the experience of the moment makes of time an integrator of the mind; but the unifying by the mind of its experience of the moment can no less be taken as an integration. That unifying of the experience of the moment is an aspect of the unity of the 'I.'"

In an imaginative, yet cautious paper, M. E. and A. B. Scheibel,[8] drawing on the work of Wilder Penfield, Moruzzi, Magoun and others, see in the

Further on we shall describe, if not define exactly, what we mean by ego. For the moment, we are concerned with ego-genesis and the imperative nature of its evolution. The evolution of the brain in man, with increasing precedence of the higher centers in determining behavior in the broadest sense of the term, created a new inner environment for which new adaptations were required. We would expect that the adaptation that was called for by a new psychological environment, i.e., consciousness, would itself be a new psychological entity or quality. It is just such a quality that we conceive ego to be.

Whenever we speak of evolutionary processes and of their hierarchical advance, we are hampered by a distorted temporal conception that is almost a part of language. We are left with the feeling that first *this* evolved, then *that;* that bipedal locomotion in man was followed by the use of the hands, then by the evolution of the brain, the use of tools, the further development of the brain, the evolution of consciousness, and finally of ego. Actually, nothing could be further from the truth, for although certain evolutionary steps are in some sense prerequisites for subsequent ones, *a linear picture of evolution* is a distortion. Organisms, and man included, evolve as a whole in a continuous interchange with the environment—both inner and outer—so that we have an intricate pattern of elaborate, interlocking processes operating over unimaginably long periods of time, the final outcome of which in any given structure or function can never be explained by a one-to-one causal relationship. In this sense, the imperative nature of ego-genesis is better under-

---

brain stem reticular core the anatomical and physiological seat of the integrative principle which we call "ego." They say: "The reticular formation is thereby continuously informed of the nature of the environment, the neural transactions going on throughout the brain, and the type of activity planned and executed to cope with the shifting environment."

stood as the product of the continuous evolutionary inter-action of rudimentary ego states with the ever-increasing complexities of conscious experience.

The importance of interaction within parts of the evolv-ing organism as well as between the organism and its environ-ment is well illustrated by the work of Beach (1947).[9] Working in the area of the study of sexual behavior, Beach has shown clearly that as encephalization and particularly neocorticalization have increased in the evolutionary hier-archy, the dependence of sexual behavior, or mating behavior particularly, on hormonal control has decreased. In lower animals, mating behavior depends on the rhythmic seasonal appearance of hormonal changes that represent a long-evolved harmonious adaptation between the species and its environ-ment. We speak of such control of behavior as instinctive. With the development of the brain and especially of the cortex in higher animals, instinctive control (cerebellar and lymbic systems) ceded to cortical control. In terms of our concern with the advent of consciousness, we might say that as evolution proceeds, sexual behavior enters more and more into the field of awareness, until in the human species it depends on an interaction between instinctive processes and the highest organization of conscious processes, namely ego. The beginnings of ego in the most rudimentary form might be placed at that point in evolution where the speci-ficity of instinctual pattern gives way to some modifiability by cortical control. That there are evolutionary changes in sexual behavior which tend to reduce dependence on the purely hormonal and place it in the sphere of cortical control, and ultimately of consciousness and ego, constitutes evi-dence not only for the biological inherency of ego, but for its phylogenetic origins.

It is further of great interest that Beach has shown that evolutionary changes in sexual behavior do not necessarily involve evolutionary changes in the pituitary and gonadal hormones themselves, but rather in the degree of "sensitivity and dependence of neural mechanisms upon the endocrine secretions," in other words, an evolution of threshold mechanisms. Such an evolutionary hierarchy of increasing sensitivity between hormonal and neural responses can become a partial basis at least of species differentiation. But within a given species, we know that there are great differences in threshold responses, in degrees of sensitivity. Such differences form the basis of individuation, and all processes of individuation, since they represent modifications and variations of the stereotypy of instinctual behavior, are precursors of ego processes. Here again in the evolution of neurophysiological interactions, namely of sensitivity patterns, we have evidence of the phylogenetic origins of ego.

All the regulatory-adaptive processes which characterize the evolution of life and which we have described earlier in this volume as resulting in the "imprisonment of time," i.e., in the absoluteness of biological time, were in all organisms up to man largely automatic. In the evolutionary ascent of the primates, there is clearly delineated an increasing accuracy, range, and organization of perception which are the concomitants of increasing complexity of the central nervous system and of its interaction with the endocrine system. But it is not until we reach the hominid level that the elaboration of the brain and nervous system endows its possessor with so wide a spectrum of consciousness that he is aware of himself and of others. The synchronization of time-space relationships with his own organism can no longer proceed solely automatically, but calls for the emergence of a new regulatory, adaptive process, which we call ego. Thus, the persistent advance of organic evolution in the area of nervous system elaboration has eventuated in a new kind of evolution: the mental or psychological. This fact has been recognized through its manifestation in socio-cultural evolution. In discussing tools and evolution, S. L. Washburn[10] says: "The rapid rate of change which appears during the time of last glacial advance is due both to the cumulative effects of culture and to the appearance of Homo Sapiens, the biological form which made culture as we know it possible. . . . Tool types change rapidly, man crosses large bodies of water, conquers the Arctic, and art appears in the archeological record. This is the record of culture, the evidence of the presence of the restless creator we know as Homo Sapiens."

This statement not only clearly links the cultural with the biological, seeing one as the outcome of the other, but describes the continuation of the evolutionary processes in the areas of cultural advance. However, neither the biological, the anthropological, nor the psychological literature account for that aspect of evolution, the mental, which must mediate between somatic advance and its ultimate external product—culture. A. I. Hallowell[11] comes closest to an awareness of psychological evolution when he writes: "The fact had been overlooked that the only way in which a culture can be perpetuated is through the characteristic psychological structuralization of individuals in an organized system of social action." Hallowell looks to the Freudian structural model of personality for the prototype of that which has evolved in the mental life of man. While we would agree with the recognition of psychological evolution, we are of the opinion that the Freudian conception of personality with its tension-reduction theory of motivation, its overemphasis on the sexual instincts, its predominantly passive conception of the human ego, is inadequate for an explanation of the evolutionary nature and phylogenetic origin of that organizational adaptive process which we call ego.

The need for a conception of an active ego as it derives from certain contradictions and limitations in Freudian theory, from the psychological data of animal and child behavior, and from a re-evaluation of psychoanalytic case material, was strongly felt by White.[12] Within the framework of psychoanalytic theory, he makes a valuable contribution to an expansion of our understanding "by introducing the idea of an active ego serving the biological purpose of competence." The energies that activate this ego are not derivatives of instinctual energies in the earlier psychoanalytic sense but are independent ego energies.

It is certainly not within the scope of this work to deal with the exceedingly complex and controversial problem of psychic energy as it was created and perpetuated by certain early hypotheses of Freud. We would nevertheless wish to make it clear that while we are in agreement with White in regard to the active principle in ego, we see no need for assuming independent ego energies. In fact, the very qualifying term "independent" would lead one to ask: "Independent of what? Of what other energies?" thus suggesting different kinds of psychic energy or behavior-specific energy —a point of view which White[12] himself discards as invalid.

Life processes derive energy from metabolic operations, i.e., through the activation of energy on a cellular level. Psychological phenomena are no less a part of life than are digestive ones, for example. They depend for energy on nerve cells. "Each living nerve cell is capable of developing energy that is propagated, as an electric current, along its own expansions."[13] The energy for ego function then derives from the energy available to the central nervous system, which in turn taps the resources of total life energy within the organism.

While it is true that ego energies are mobilized in the name of feelings of efficacy and competence, as White convincingly argues, it would seem to us too limited a concept to explain the "biological purpose" of an action ego.

From an evolutionary point of view, the fact of competence within a certain range in the name of survival is implied by definition for any structure or function which has survived selection pressures in a given environmental situation. We would broaden the conceptions of efficacy and competence in the light which is thrown upon the emergence of ego as a product of evolution—both its organic substratum and its further psychosocial evolution—to include more than the competent performance of an individual act. In this perspective, the idea of competence would approximate the self-actualizing tendency of ego as it seeks to fulfill optimally the totality of its functions, and as it participates in the psychosocial process of evolution.

Thus, the model for ego function is to be sought not in any specific energic concept, but in the momentum of the total process of evolution.

We see the rudiments of ego as having origins coincidental with the emergence of awareness, of becoming consolidated into the form of ego of man through the biological evolutionary pressures created by neurophysiological elaboration and the existence of complex states of consciousness, and of continuing to undergo a process of evolution of another type, namely nongenetic sociocultural evolution, as a result of selection pressures exerted by the interaction of culture forms on the plastic nature of ego processes.

What is the quality or process in man to which we refer as ego? Like all mental and psychological processes, its reality is not quantitatively measurable, nor, as we have said above, can it be reduced to mechanistic terms. This does not, however, detract from its reality. We would be unwilling to call it a construct—which is the custom in dealing with psycho-

logical realities, as if by using this term and creating a termi-
nological pseudo-reality we apologize for our scientific attempts to deal with the intangible, the nonmaterial. But ego
is a reality in the life of man, as much a reality as any of his
other concepts or symbols. Symbolic reality is the characteristic of man's mental life, and it is exemplified most dramatically in the evolution of language. It is precisely the
capacity to think and to express himself in symbols that
distinguishes man's consciousness from that of other animals
and that has opened up to him a whole new kind of psychological and cultural evolution. Would we deny the reality
of this? *Ego generally observable in behavior and thought is
the symbolic reality which expresses man's awareness of his
conscious functioning.* It is therefore a reality of subjective
experience. However, in the course of individual development, not all aspects of ego function are conscious. Some are
automatized or unconscious from the beginning of life; others
become so as a consequence of learning or of the dynamics
of intrapsychic conflict.

We have tried to show that the complexities of human
consciousness called for a psychic entity that would organize
consciousness into an adaptively functioning whole, and this
entity we have called *ego*. But ego is not only that which
organizes and regulates. It is in itself a system of psychic
organization in function, the product of phylogenetic evolution and ontogenetic development, and it is therefore subject
to change. These changes in ego are not only individual,
developmental ones but they fulfill in certain respects the
criteria of evolutionary advance.

The capacity to form ego in the course of growth and
maturation, i.e., to synthesize individual environmental experience with phylogenetic inheritance is as *species-characteristic* for man as is his bipedal locomotion, his opposable
thumb, or his ability to record experience through the verbal

symbolization of memory traces. The ability thus to make use of experience is commonly referred to as learning. It is the ego which learns, but it is also ego itself which in turn is changed and molded by the learning experience.

As the evolutionary hierarchy proceeds to ever more complex forms of life, the potentiality for individuation is increased by virtue of the greater number of possible combinations and recombinations of genetic traits. In the human species, this potentiality has reached its highest point, and this individuation is not only marked in its physical manifestations so that no two individuals, unless they are identical twins, are exactly alike, but most especially in the psychological realm. We usually attribute this to the fact that the environment and experience of each individual is different from birth, and this is indeed true. We would not be surprised at a statement which described the ego as the most individuated aspect of personality. But we are accustomed to regard this as the product of specific individual growth and maturation, i.e., of ontogeny. The basis for the individuation of ego, however, is given in the phylogenetic substratum of ego organization and is manifest from birth in differences in awareness, sensitivity, reactivity, intelligence, vigor of the instinctual life, to mention several. It is these genetically determined components of ego processes, the ego nucleus as it were, which then come to interact with the environment to produce a unique individual with a highly individuated ego as we perceive it.

Individuation is not just a by-product of the on-going processes of evolution. It has itself evolved as a means of more firmly guaranteeing the survival of species. Differences in the adaptability of individual organisms within a species ensure the survival of the best fitted within a given environment. Thus, individuation becomes a statistical guarantee of species survival. Since the ego represents the most individuated aspect of personality in man, its very individuation plays a major role in his survival as a species and in his further evolution. Within the enormous range of differences in the quality of ego among the individuals of a given human population, there lies not only the possibility of greater adaptation in the more passive sense of this term, but the opportunity for the creation, through the medium of culture, of new niches for the expansion of differing ego forms which in turn have their effect on the future evolution of culture and personality. It is in this way that individuation, itself a product of organic evolution, plays a major role in the further cultural and psychological evolution of man. This ultimate example of the survival advantage of elaboration and complexity—a process which is the essence of evolutionary advance—provides in man the opportunity for advance through new levels of ego effectiveness, strength, and autonomy.

▪ REFERENCES

1. Clark, W. E. LeGros: *The Antecedents of Man*. Qaudrangle Books, Chicago, 1960, pp. 228, 229, 232-233.
2. Herrick, C. J.: *The Evolution of Human Nature*. University of Texas Press, Austin, 1956, pp. 290, 292.
3. Butler, R. A.: Curiosity in monkeys. *Scientific American*, Feb., 1954.
4. Whitehead, A. N.: *Process and Reality*. New York, 1929. (Quoted in Herrick, C. J.,[2] p. 160.)
5. Washburn, S. L., and Avis, V.: Evolution of human behavior. In Roe, A., and Simpson, G. G., Eds.: *Behavior and Evolution*. Yale University Press, New Haven, 1958, p. 435.
6. Agar, W. E.: *A Contribution to the Theory of the Living Organism*. Quoted in Sinnott, Edmund W.: A common

basis for development and behavior in organisms. *Evolution of Nervous Control From Primitive Organisms to Man.* A.A.A.'S. Washington, 1959, p. 3.

7. Sherrington, Sir C.: *Man on His Nature.* Doubleday, New York, 1955, p. 222.

8. Scheibel, M. E., and A. B.: The physiology of consciousness. *American Journal of Orthopsychiatry,* Vol. *30*: pp. 10-14, Jan., 1960.

9. Beach, F. A.: Evolutionary aspects of psychoendocrinology. In Roe, A., and Simpson, G. G., Eds.: *Behavior and Evolution.* Yale University Press, New Haven, 1958, p. 83.

10. Washburn, S. L.: Tools and evolution. In Spuhler, J. N., Ed.: *The Evolution of Man's Capacity for Culture.* Wayne State University Press, Detroit, 1959, pp. 21-31.

11. Hallowell, A. I.: Self, society and culture in phylogenetic perspective. In Tax, S., Ed.: *The Evolution of Man, Evolution After Darwin,* Vol. II. Chicago, 1960, p. 361.

12. White, R. W.: *Ego and Reality in Psychoanalytic Theory.* Psychological Issues, Vol. III, No. 3, Monograph 11. International Universities Press, New York, 1963, pp. 175-180.

13. Penfield, W., and Roberts, L.: *Speech and Brain-Mechanisms.* Princeton University Press, Princeton, N. J., 1959, p. 5.

8 · THE NEW PATIENT

LET US turn from the more theoretical aspects of the evolution of ego in psychobiological terms to a discussion of evolutionary change in the personalities we encounter in psychotherapeutic work and the present-day social situation which serves as a medium for their development.

By the present-day "social situation," we mean our modern Western culture and all it includes: technological advances and consequent economic changes, changes in social structuring and social institutions, scientific, ethical, and artistic progress, and advances in psychological knowledge and understanding. We have earlier stated that the creation of what we have broadly called "culture," is based in man's biological evolution and then in turn becomes the medium for further nongenetic evolution. Innumerable works have dealt with cultural evolution, and it is not within the purpose of this work to follow the intricately winding stream of cultural advance and its gathering momentum up to the present time. Rather, we prefer to take that small segment of the modern scene which is our chief concern, namely the development of psychoanalysis as it has influenced psychotherapy, and to show how its evolution within the social milieu has changed that milieu and man interacting in it.

In order to make our point as clear as possible, let us make an analogy between the emergence of psychoanalysis and the invention of the automobile. The first essential step was, of course, the invention of the combustion engine. Once this principle had been discovered, the new source of energy was harnessed to the old vehicle, the carriage, so that the first automobiles were truly "horseless carriages." Through a succession of improvements, the "evolution" of the automobile as we know it today took place. The engine was improved for greater speed, a self-starter was introduced, the chassis was built for greater comfort and less air resistance, and finally aesthetic factors played a role in what became the modern car. But the purpose of our analogy is not merely to point out the improvements in the newly developed apparatus itself, but to show how its own evolution changed the society in which it grew and the persons within this society. The existence of the automobile called for the building of more and better roads. More roads created the opportunity for the growth of population centers in areas that were formerly isolated. Communication and trade increased. People's knowledge of other places and people increased; their world of experience broadened. Even the pattern of social life was changed. Families did not have to live so close to one another to maintain contact. Young adults, therefore, achieved greater independence without having to pay the price of a complete break with family. Patterns of courtship and socializing among young people came to depend on the automobile. Modern medical care became available to people who would not otherwise have enjoyed it. Contact with cultural life, books, art, and theater was made possible for individuals living in smaller communities. From the impact of these man-made environmental changes, some changes occurred in personality also. Feelings about time and space inevitably were modified, and man felt a greater mastery of both. Certain kinds of anxiety were diminished since there was less physical isolation and an expansion of opportunities for enterprise. Enjoyment and recreation were more immediately available with the consequent positive and negative implications for the development of personality. It is not necessary to elaborate further on all the details of the changes brought about by the appearance and further development of the automobile to make it clear that this invention created a new milieu which opened up new niches for the physical development of life and for concomitant psychological change, and further that the progress of these changes has taken place at an astonishing speed, and with ever-gathering momentum.

Could new understanding of the nature of man, a new theory of personality, also revolutionize life and contribute to its evolutionary advance? The emergence of psychoanalysis and its dissemination has had just such an effect. Psychoanalysis in its early beginnings was a method for curing the neuroses, notably hysteria, and to that end it applied its newly won understanding of the existence of the unconscious and of repression as the critical factors in symptom formation. It attempted to abolish the pathognomic repressions through the method of free association. Out of this—in retrospect—relatively schematic understanding and procedure grew a modern psychoanalytic body of psychological theory which includes a theory of human motivation, a structural conception of personality, a theory of instinct, and a general and special theory of the neuroses. Considerable technical advances in the application of this body of psychological theory to the problems of treatment were also made. The evolution of psychoanalytic thought proceeded not only from within the ranks of the original followers of Freud and their descendants, but from so-called dissident groups who often made significant contributions to our further understanding of human personality and to the treatment of its disorders. Without going into a discussion of the relative merits of varying "schools" of psychoanalytic thought, it will serve our purpose to say that psychoanalysis, like the automobile, evolved on the basis of experience, investigation, research, and the speculative imagination of gifted individuals into a body of knowledge that was cohesive enough to make its dissemination possible. It took the course of all scientific and technological development and became part of the man-made environment which was to still further influence man's social and psychological evolution.

The rapid and extensive advance of psychoanalysis and its application in psychotherapy, as well as its broad dissemination throughout the population, did not take place evenly throughout Western culture. In most of the more tradition-bound countries of Europe, its progress has been very slow, and its application has been more specifically confined to the treatment of individual cases of mental illness. In the United States, on the other hand, the social fabric is less rigid, customs and mores are more varied and flexible, there is latitude for the introduction and development of new ideas. Evolutionarily speaking, there are unfilled niches; there is room for expansion. Here, psychoanalysis has had an effect on many important aspects of life and on basic social institutions. A comparison of the Bulletin issued by the U.S.

Department of Labor on infant care in the early thirties with the book on the same subject by Benjamin Spock, which has now become the authority for many young American mothers, will reveal the influence of psychoanalytic thinking, the effect of which has flooded the country in ten short years.

First of all, psychoanalysis as a historical theory and method emphasized that what happened in childhood *did* matter and did have an effect on later life. To the extent that this point of view was absorbed in the population, it counteracted the previous notions of childhood as an amorphous, half-conscious period of life in which nothing made a very deep impression and most difficulties were outgrown, leaving no imprint on adult life. Once the idea was accepted that the experiences of childhood had a bearing on the nature and behavior of the mature adult, child-rearing procedures were changed and the parental feeling of responsibility augmented. That this fact, in certain respects, has had negative effects of making parents overanxious, self-conscious, and guilt-ridden, and has tended to provide children with a rationalization for shunning their own responsibility in the adjustment to the demands of life, is relatively minor in comparison to the gains achieved: The importance of the affectional bond with the parents, especially the mother, to the physical and emotional development of the infant from the beginning of life was established; thumb sucking, smearing, exploratory behavior, curiosity were understood not as bad habits or nuisances to be gotten rid of, but as expressions of normal instinctual behavior for certain levels of development; the anxieties of childhood were also recognized as normal aspects of development to be handled with understanding rather than with the critical, judgmental attitudes of former times; the developing ego of the child and his wish for but apprehensive attitude toward independence were comprehended as needing nurturing and encouragement. That siblings have normal antagonisms as well as affection for one another is today accepted. In fact, the phenomenon of hateful feelings toward someone whom one also loves is no longer regarded as an aberration, but as a normal problem in the tasks of living. It is now more generally accepted that not all thoughts and emotions are conscious, that there can exist unconscious feelings of which we only get hints through dreams or daydreams, for example. We owe to psychoanalysis this extension of our knowledge of how human personality develops and functions.

The role of parent, then, in the framework of these new insights has a quality different from that of forty years ago, and the child reared under these auspices has a different conception of himself and of his relationship to others. The psychological character of the family in certain segments of Western society has been modified. In extending the area of human knowledge and therefore the range of experience, the first criterion for evolutionary progress in the psychological realm has been met; consciousness has been enlarged; therefore, ego has expanded and grown in intricacy to encompass new association areas, as well as the newly acquired awareness of the unconscious. This extension of ego function calls for greater ego autonomy to fulfill the demands of new functions, and so one evolutionary step leads to another. Just as the invention of the combustion engine set in motion the evolution of the automobile, which subsequently affected the evolution of social institutions, so the discoveries of psychoanalysis, through their dissemination and application in America in fields other than the immediate treatment of psychiatric problems, led not only to evolutionary advances within the science of psychology itself, but to social changes which must influence the quality and nature of ego that is growing and interacting in the new milieu.

Out of the new social matrix of which psychoanalysis and

its effects are a part, there has evolved a new type of patient who is identifiable by the *nature of his motivation* to psychotherapy; the patient who is aware of the nature of his conscious conflict and goals in therapy and who assumes active responsibility for change represents an evolutionary advance in the function of ego. Obviously, not all patients who seek treatment exemplify the advance of which we speak; in fact, it will perhaps clarify our point if we contrast individual cases with different motivation.

P. is a patient of the "old type." He might indeed have been one of Freud's first cases, for he suffers from anxiety hysteria. But it is not the particular diagnostic category into which he falls that makes him in our mind an "old-fashioned patient." It is the way in which his ego functions as it relates to the task of treatment, to his conception of himself and of the therapist, to his general attitudes about people and life—all of which are reflected in his motivation toward psychotherapy. P. is a businessman whose work often demands that he leave his home town. Within the year preceding the beginning of his treatment, he had experienced increasingly frequent and severe anxiety attacks whenever he had to make a business trip. The farther they were from home, the greater the anxiety. He was indeed overwhelmed by feelings of panic which came upon him suddenly and in the most unexpected situations and places. Needless to say, he suffered greatly not only from the anxiety itself, which interfered with his work, but also from an utter feeling of helplessness in the face of it. In addition, he was unhappily married, had several small children of whom he was genuinely fond, and was plagued by indecision about whether to continue the marriage. Actually, his psychosexual development was arrested; he was unable to relate in a consistent and mature way to his wife, was given to sexual varietism as a way of assuring himself that he was an adequate man, and had a tendency to be sadistic with women. In general, his human relationships were characterized by a predominant focus on his own needs and a lack of empathy and understanding of the other person. He was a lonely man who suffered and was made fearful by his isolation.

Yet, in more superficial encounters he evinced a warmth, honesty, directness, and childlike openness that made him decidedly likeable and served him exceedingly well in business relationships. His work life was successful and brought him considerable satisfaction, especially since he had created and built up his business entirely through his own efforts.

Had he not had crippling anxiety attacks, it is doubtful whether he would ever have sought psychotherapy. He assumed that his unhappy marriage was just a piece of bad luck, and that if indeed his own character structure contributed to it in any measure, this was just the way he was. The possibility of fundamental change and growth was foreign to his thinking. Thus, he approached treatment much as a patient with a physical ailment might approach a physician—prepared to describe his ailment, to be questioned about it, to receive advice and a prescription, to follow instructions, and then hopefully to experience cure.

One could analyze the unconscious childhood components in his individual life history that contributed to his immature character structure and to his anxiety without fundamentally changing the passive position of his ego in relation to the therapist and to all authority figures—a passivity reflected in his motivation toward treatment and his way of approaching it. True, he was the victim of a broken home, having lost his father through the separation of his parents at an early age; true, he was overattached to his mother, a situation which presented him with great identification conflicts in adolescence and early adulthood when every individual attempts to consolidate his own identity. However, neither these facts nor many other details of his early experience serve to explain the passive position of his ego. A classical psychoanalytic explanation of the nature of his relationship to authority figures would emphasize the persistence of a longing for a submissive relationship to a father whom he had scarcely known, and lacking this, a regression to a dependent relationship to mother figures who would fulfill his emotional needs. Further, a failure on his part to implement these explanations in the course of treatment and a continuance of the passive demand on the therapist—"Cure me; tell me what to do"—would be interpreted as resistance to the treatment, as unwillingness to make use of the insight acquired through the uncovering of unconscious needs and wishes. Such explanations have their measure of truth and are important steps in the course of treatment. They do not, however, elucidate sufficiently the nature of the causality involved in the passive nature of this patient's ego. If they did, we would be justified in expecting their analysis to effect changes in ego quality; empirically, this was not the case.

Granted this individual had a traumatic childhood which played a role in the outcome of his adult personality; this represents but one aspect of the intricate patterning of causality that resulted in the passive nature of his ego. How then are we, in terms of our evolutionary thinking, prepared to explain it?

First, let us be clear that whatever the reasons, P. is, at least in important interpersonal relationships, a passive individual and that this becomes evident in his motivation toward cure and in his functioning in life as well as in therapy. We assume that we are dealing with an inherent, constitutional ego quality of relative inactivity, which was reinforced by early childhood experience and that this interaction then conspired to make it difficult for this individual to take advantage of new niches which his psychosocial environment (his psychotherapy being one such niche) offered for ego activity and expansion. By inherent ego quality, we would envisage all psychophysical attributes that tend to heighten the predisposition to anxiety and thereby to inhibit the normal evolutionary striving of ego processes. It is not that P.'s neurotic difficulties, his anxiety hysteria, for example, are to be accounted for in constitutional terms, but that his attitude toward them, his wish for help to come almost exclusively from the outside, his view of himself as a rather passive victim of life, his willingness to be content with the status quo of his own personality structure provided someone would show him how to avoid unhappiness reveal the innate absence of striving toward improvement that characterize ego processes on the move. Were P. a Stone Age man, it is doubtful that he himself would have invented the ax, but he would have made excellent ones according to the model invented by the head of the clan.

It is important to emphasize that there is nothing judgmental in our characterization of this patient, nor are we implying that he cannot be helped in psychotherapy. If, however, we do not take into account the intrinsic nature of his ego, we may make serious errors in interpretation and in the concept of causality which we transmit to the patient. In a later chapter, we will deal concretely with the importance of estimating the inherent ego quality of a patient in psychotherapy. Here, let us say that this quality is a "given"; it is a manifestation of the evolutionary fact of individuation whose negative implications (if we may call them such, namely that the great majority of individuals serve, in the course of their development, the conservative, stabilizing aspects of evolution rather than the progressive, forward-moving ones) must be given due weight.

Patients whose neurotic conflicts are expressed in clearly

symptomatic form tend to be motivated toward therapy predominantly in terms of relief of symptoms. R. is another such patient. He suffered from hysterical nausea and vomiting and digestive symptoms of a psychogenic nature. The symptoms were the precipitates of unconscious conflicts stemming from his childhood history. When he was five years old, his father died of cancer of the stomach; as an only son in a family of several older sisters, he was at once spoiled and dominated by them, and by his mother. At the point in puberty where the striving for selfhood is paramount, hysterical symptoms and conscious anxiety appeared. Like the small child who is afraid to leave home and go to school in the morning, and expresses his anxiety by vomiting, R. expressed the growing fear of separation, which maturation implied, in the hysterical symptom. As is generally the case, the symptom was multidetermined in terms of its psychodynamic origins. It included an identification with his father through the illness "in the stomach"; it expressed anger and rage at his mother and sisters through the attempt to eject what they had forced on him; it expressed guilt for this very anger which he felt as his inability to be sufficiently grateful for the kind of love that his mother did give him.

In his adult work life his initiative was inhibited. He attached himself to his sister's husband and worked in his business in a subordinate capacity. The patient was keenly aware of the anxieties and dependency needs that prevented him from striking out alone in an area of his own interest; part of his motivation toward psychotherapy went beyond the passive wish to be freed of his symptoms and included the wish for help to free his ego to find its own niche in the working world. His aspirations, however, did not go beyond this. He was content with the extent of his knowledge and education, his value system, the nature of his interaction with others, and his goals in life. He wanted to be able to lead the average life of a man of average success in the limited social world in which he functioned. This, his therapy made possible for him, for it resolved the unconscious conflicts that were responsible for his symptoms and provided for him a father substitute, the therapist, with whom he could identify, thus consolidating his masculine identity and enabling him to achieve a marked measure of independence in his work life. His was not, however, a personality characterized by a wish to go very far beyond the traditions which he knew, to assert an individuality that in any marked way (unless it was perhaps in the area of economic success) expressed either a deviation from his origins or a new way of understanding or synthesizing experience.

B. is a young woman who presents quite a different picture, the "new patient" whose actively searching ego is on the alert for any and all opportunities which the environment offers for expansion, change, resynthesis, and reintegration. This is already revealed in the way she chooses her analyst, a fact which we learned about later in treatment. She consulted several people before finally deciding on her therapist and made the choice on the basis of a conscious awareness that she needed a female analyst whose values and personality structure would offer her a model on which to build her own personality, since to her mind her mother had proved to be inadequate in this respect.

Some psychogenic digestive disturbances and an unsatisfactory marriage were the precipitating causes of her seeking treatment, but they were in fact just that. B. knew that she wanted to change, that she wanted not only to be rid of her anxieties, but to be respected at work, not to be exploited by friends who took advantage of her good nature; she wanted to be able to make decisions, to be able to love with a full awareness of the individuality of the other person, and to be loved this way in return. She wanted to be fully expressive as a woman and as an intellectual individual. To these ends, she mobilized all her available ego energies. She was determined to use these energies to change, in a fundamental way, the very qualitative nature of her ego itself. This "bootstrap" operation was particularly dramatic and instructive in this case because her childhood situation and the personality of her mother conspired so effectively to create a dependent, anxious, masochistic character structure, which could only have been countered, to produce the individual whom we knew, by the strongly evolving nature of her inherent ego quality. Her early childhood experiences played a large part in creating her neurosis, but her innate ego and its ability to find, create, and use environmental opportunity played an equally large part in her recovery and in her further development as a rich, expressive, and forward-moving personality.

B. was brought into the world unwillingly by a hysterical, anxious, and ignorant mother who lived within the narrow conventions of her group and whose greatest fear was that these might be transgressed by her growing daughter. She resented and dreaded any and every expression of independence in her child, including even the earliest maturational processes such as walking and talking. Her violent outbursts of rage terrified B. and inhibited her activity. There was but one area open for the expansion of her personality and ego functions, and that was in the intellectual sphere. It was at school that B. excelled, and it was through her educational endeavors that she acquired the knowledge that freed her from her mother's superstitions and opened up new social opportunities which brought new ideologies and new ways of thinking to her attention. It was through her newly acquired friends that she learned of psychoanalysis; she read some of the psychoanalytic literature and participated in discussion groups in which psychological and social problems were discussed. An awareness of the existence of psychoanalysis in the milieu with which she made contact, as it interacted with the striving of her own ego, helped her to outgrow her own milieu, leave home, continue her studies, marry, and ultimately seek psychoanalytic help.

Despite the great strides which a personality such as B. made relative to her original environment, the traumatic experiences of her early life, especially in relation to her mother, left deep scars, left much to be overcome and to be worked through in her treatment. The seeming paradox of her personality was that although she actively combated her anxieties and dependencies, she retained an unconscious bond with and a fear of separation from her mother, which inhibited the full development of her ego potentialities; it was with this that she needed and used help.[1] Interestingly enough, the help came much more in the form of correcting her perceptions of her mother (she had held on to distortions of her mother image and of her self-image in order to uphold the bond and avoid separation), an extension of an ego function, than in the unearthing of unconscious wishes and impulses.

B. knew that she was unable to make a sufficient commitment to another person, to experience enough basic trust to love another human being fully. She experienced this, after the breakup of her marriage, insofar as it was difficult for her to establish satisfactory relationships with men. Throughout the long years of struggle, however, what was outstanding was the clarity of her goal, her ability to conceptualize accurately the nature of a truly loving relationship which included much more a concern with her ability to give of herself than to receive, and a determination to fulfill or approximate in reality her imagined ideal. Whether it was in her role as a loving wife or her contemplation of the prospect of motherhood, an area in which her lack of spontaneous impulse troubled her, she demanded of herself that she evolve the capacity to fill these roles happily in a way in which her mother never succeeded in doing, and that she be able to integrate them with other aspects of her life and activity. The demand placed on the self to strive toward a conceptualized and projected goal and the ability to use the environment toward these ends characterize the evolving ego. The new patient consciously "wills" to advance in an environment which has provided a sufficient glimpse of new opportunities to mobilize the ever forward-moving forces of ego.

In a young male patient, the struggle between the evolving ego forces and the passive wish to be cured through an incorporation of the therapist's personality is more evenly matched than in B., though the final outcome seems to favor an advance that goes beyond the overcoming of his neurosis. G. sought out psychotherapy because of a clearly conscious awareness that the routine work which he was doing did not correspond to his innate talent and ability and was therefore entirely unsatisfying to him. His anxiety and inhibition in providing himself fulfillment and self-realization were rooted in his emotional dependence on a domineering and autocratic father who considered any activity beyond that required for making an adequate living entirely superfluous. Our patient was in opposition to his father's values and was eager to leave home, but his striving ego needed the help and support of the therapist. That he possessed considerable talent in the field of music lent a specific goal and content to the forward-moving impetus of his ego which had found expression in the search for psychotherapy. Here again, the existing environment provided the opportunity not only for overcoming his neurotic inhibitions and for supporting his ego strivings in search of his own appropriate niche through the treatment, but also of actually finding this niche within the societal setting. Because ours is still an expanding society, we can see an evolutionary process (less apparent in more static societies)—the interaction of ego, on the move in an individual case, with the openings existing in the societal structure. This actual "niche search" which played a central role in G.'s motivation toward psychotherapy and determined the nature of his conflict during treatment leads us to also call him a "new patient."

There will certainly be those in a given population who are evolving personalities but who are by no means necessarily patients. We, as therapists, experience these processes of psychosocial evolution within the confines of a patient population, but, as we have already indicated,* throughout history, throughout every culture, there are those individuals who strive to transcend the psychological niche of their original milieu, to take advantage of new cultural opportunities, and in the ego synthesis which results, to find personal balance and perhaps make a social contribution.

The psychological evolution of which we speak goes hand in hand with social change which also moves in a generally advancing direction. Often, the direction of these changes and the opportunities which they offer for the expansion of certain areas of ego function create new ego ideals and goals for the individual which may produce new conflicts and anxieties. For example, E. was able to use the opportunities which her milieu offered and her native intelligence to achieve a high degree of success in her career as an editor in a large publishing house. After some psychotherapeutic help, she was able to marry successfully, but she was filled with the fear that she had insufficient maternal impulse. To the psychoanalytically trained psychologist, the very existence of this fear would be proof enough that there were neurotic conflicts inhibiting the maternal impulse which had their origins in the life history of this individual. Perhaps E. had not accepted her female role; perhaps her life was too overwhelm-

* Cf. Chapter V.

ingly dominated by masculine strivings. But if we extend our concept of causality to include an intricate patterned interaction of social and psychological forces seen in the light of evolutionary movement, then we are in a position to broaden our understanding of a person like E. and her conflict.*

A socially accepted ideal of the young American professional woman is to be a good mother and successful in her chosen vocation. This social ideal from which the young woman derives a large part of her self-image—or to use Erikson's[2] term, her "identity"—is in itself part of a recent sociocultural evolutionary process which is not as yet consolidated. There are still many elements in our social structure that look askance at this new role of woman; even some psychoanalytic opinion has been used to rationalize a critical attitude toward it.[3]

The conflict of E., then, is much more than a neurotic striving for the male role. It expresses the fear that she will not be able to integrate the new area of functioning, her career, with other areas of ego function or instinctual need. The problem in integration is posed for her ego by the social and personal advances to which she is exposed, and its solution constitutes part of the evolutionary process in which she is a participant.

Does it seem reasonable to assume that new processes of synthesis and integration with which the ego of an individual is faced and which we have called evolutionary should be accompanied by anxiety? Certainly, we cannot assume that the inconceivably long and gradual accretions of the processes of organic evolution were attended by anxiety. In the animal world from which we emerged, anxiety—or shall we say, fear—serves a survival function and appears as a warning

---

* William Menaker, in a paper read at the New York Society of Clinical Psychologists in 1959, stressed the importance of culturally evolving factors in assessing feminine conflict.

of impending danger to be reacted to with the full panoply of automatic instinctual equipment which is available for the individual's survival. Human evolution poses a new problem, although it is motivated by the same survival need. It is obvious that the great human evolutionary acquisition, awareness, must add a special dimension to fear. Very simply, where there is more knowledge, there is more to be afraid of.* But the conscious extension of time and space dimensions into the past and future and the retention of human experience in remembered, symbolic form add to the area in which anxiety can flourish. It is impossible to be conscious without being conscious of dangers of all sorts, and it is in fact one of the functions of consciousness to serve survival through the awareness of anxiety. We have made the point earlier that the task of synthesizing and integrating all the varying aspects of conscious experience, translating them into thought or action, falls to ego. In the individual life history, every maturational step in development, i.e., every new acquisition of ego function, is accompanied by a mixture of pleasure and satisfaction on the one hand and anxiety on the other. One has but to watch the jubilant expression on the face of the very young child, who has gotten to his feet and made his first step with the help of some object or piece of furniture in the room, change to one of mild consternation as he wonders how he will negotiate the distance between this supporting object and the next, to realize what a mixed experience growth is. The ego can only synthesize and make part of itself that which has already been experienced; in other words, what can be remembered. What is as yet unexperienced, i.e., new, is not yet a part of the ego, has therefore not been mastered, and must produce anxiety. Yet, with the passage of time the organic forces of development inevitably unfold,

---

* Knowledge, of course, also becomes a way of mastering anxiety.

social interaction is broadened, learning tasks grow more complex, emotional experiences become more involved, and the work life grows more demanding. In the course of the individual life cycle, the ego is presented with an almost unending series of integrative tasks which are quite normally preceded by anxiety.

However, the human creature is confronted not only with the task of synthesizing his individual life experiences and mastering the anxiety which inevitably accompanies this process. He is a particle in the stream of the sociocultural aspect of phylogenetic evolution, and all the changes and developments within this moving stream impinge upon him as new forces and experiences—experiences which call for integration and which, in the course of the process, create anxiety. Our patient E. experienced the impact of newly evolved social goals for women in fearing that she would be unable to integrate them with other strivings in her life. Added to the many conflicting facets of her ontogeny which were undoubtedly important factors in producing a neurotic character structure is the evolving social scene which created additional anxiety, but which also, on the positive side, produced those pressures which called for ego changes within her personality, and which were therefore instrumental in her psychological evolution.

The new conflicts and problems in synthesis which an evolving social structure presents to our patients are present for the total population at any given time or place, and the evolutionary advances which take place in individuals as well as in groups are not confined to our patients. We deal with them here as examples of evolutionary progress because they have come to our attention through our psychotherapeutic work and because the very fact of seeking help, involving as it does a realization of a gap between individual development and ultimate goals, is often a manifestation of that ego striving toward synthesis which we regard as evolutionary.

The evolving individual, patient or not, does not inevitably have a less conflictful life experience. Quite the contrary; the awareness of the necessity of unifying the constituent parts of his individual experience and all the conflict that this might include—with the evolutionary advances of his society as they impinge upon him in all conceivable forms, from technological advance to psychological discoveries—constitutes an added task for the ego which takes energy, courage, and plasticity, and whose inevitable by-product is conflict and anxiety.

We regard the "new patient" as an individual whose consciousness has been extended to include the new knowledge of psychoanalysis and psychology and who is more prepared than most of his predecessors or contemporaries to actively take responsibility for implementing this knowledge to achieve more effective ego organization and autonomy through his own efforts. He thus brings into the therapeutic situation an ego moved by evolutionary striving, a fact of great moment when we come to consider the impact of our point of view for therapeutic procedures.

▪ REFERENCES

1. Menaker, E.: Masochism: a defense reaction of the ego. *Psychoanalytic Quarterly, 22:* 205-220, 1953.
2. Erikson, E. H.: *Childhood and Society.* W. W. Norton, New York, 1950.
3. Friedan, B.: *The Feminine Mystique.* W. W. Norton, New York, 1963.

9 ▪ THE SOCIAL MATRIX AND THE

STRUCTURING OF EGO

For ALL organisms, the environment is the matrix in which they are enveloped, in relation to which they grow and with which they continue to interact throughout their life cycles. The mold and what is molded form one interdependent unit. For almost all organisms, the parent is at some point in development and for some time the physical and biological environment of the offspring. This is the nature of life's ability to duplicate, to reproduce itself. The seed is at first housed in the parent plant; the egg develops in the body of the hen; the lion cub and the human infant grow in the mother's womb. As organisms evolve greater complexity, however,

the gap widens both in time and in environmental require-
ment between embryonic development and the emergence
of the mature individual. The parent, primarily the mother,
remains an essential part of the environment for an increasingly longer period, the higher we ascend the animal scale.
This simple and easily observable fact is a positive function
of the increased complexity of neurophysiological processes.
The intricacy of reactivity and responsiveness to environment, reflected in increased perceptual sensitivity, in complex
behavior, and finally in thought, conceptualization, verbal
communication, and emotional responsiveness in man, cannot
be completed *in utero*. For the maturation of neural equipment, for its efficient functioning by way of a variety of
learning experiences at different evolutionary levels, the social
matrix evolved.

The course of human evolution and therefore of survival
has, in organic terms, taken the direction of the elaboration
of brain and nervous systems to the point of the emergence of
conscious awareness. The long road to these evolutionary
gains has been described in great detail by Gerard:[1] "Sensory
thresholds have fallen, by a million, million fold, and sensory
range and discrimination have risen; and responses have
similarly vastly improved in speed and power and discrete-
ness. These improvements were achieved primarily at the
cellular level, by better receptor and effector elements, and
were largely or entirely completed with the appearance of
arthropods and vertebrates. Even the basic conducting nerve
fiber, transmitting synapse, and integrating neurone had
reached their asymptote in the lowest vertebrate, with fast
all-or-none conduction, irreciprocal transmission, and reflex
facilitation and inhibition. Further gains, mainly in the
patterning and generalization of experience and in the variability and modifiability of behavior, came from increased

numbers of elements—the neurones of the central nervous system." Exactly how the change from quantitative increase in brain size and number of neurones to the qualitative change, the appearance of consciousness, has taken place is not known. There is some difference of opinion among neurophysiologists[2] as to whether the evolutionary leap is the result simply of augmentations which in themselves were responsible for the appearance of new elements, or whether some entirely new, and as yet unknown factors were at work. Whatever the case may be, we might add that from the implementation of an evolutionary point of view an understanding of the emergence of consciousness cannot be arrived at through the most detailed knowledge of the nervous system alone, highly important as this is, but through an understanding of man's total functioning in and interaction with his physical, biological, and social environments. When Washburn and Avis[3] refer to the effect of handedness on brain size, their thinking goes in the direction of such a holistic approach which sees evolutionary advance as the product of the synergistic effect of many interacting causalities which operate in the functioning of the total organism in its biosphere.

Out of the elaboration of nervous system to the point of awareness, we have derived the evolution of ego—a phylogenetically evolved psychic apparatus which becomes for each individual the focal point for the synthesis of all the special human functions of consciousness: attention, symbolic conceptualization and speech, memory, differentiation, reintegration, modifiability, insight and insightful behavior, thought and awareness of self. This general statement, however, tells us nothing of the process by which ego matures from the amorphous psychic state of the helpless infant to the point of self-awareness and subsequent autonomous thought and action.

All organizations exist in the organism at its inception as a template (a patterned organization *in potentio**) which in the proper environment unfolds to become that which corresponds to the information which is carried. In the human neonate, this is the case for many functions: locomotion, hand-eye co-ordination, and speech, to mention a few. The extreme helplessness of the infant and the long period of childhood dependency are testimony to the incompleteness of nervous organization at birth. For the maturation of the nervous system as well as for the formation of ego, a specific social environment, the mother-child biota, is required. It has been shown that when this is absent, insufficient, or when no adequate mother substitute has been provided, the infant may suffer irreparable damage to the nervous system or may even not survive.[5] The deleterious effects of maternal deprivation on neurological maturation and on subsequent behavior have been extensively demonstrated in the case of animals.[7, 8, 9, 10]† In the human species, maternal deprivation occurs in varying degrees, from complete physical absence to insufficient tenderness, care, affection, love, and understanding. The distinguishing common denominator, however, is the absence or insufficiency of communication and contact between mother and offspring.

There is clear evidence that the need to communicate information to other members within a species appears early among the vertebrates, and that such communication is linked to the carrying out of functions crucial to survival.

---

* Gerard[1] refers in this connection to epigenesis, and Erikson[4] speaks of the epigenetic principle. (See also Spitz, R.[5])

† Philip F. D. Seitz states:[6] "Early infantile traumata have persistent effects upon adult behavior, lasting throughout the lifetime of the animal and affecting practically every modality of behavior that is tested. These findings correspond with the principle of development discovered in experimental embryology; the earlier a trauma occurs in the development of an organism, the greater the number of structures that are affected by it."

Thus, in speaking of birds, Lorenz[11] comments that whether in relation to courtship, mating, feeding the young, nest-building, or fight for dominance, "many of these motor patterns have evolved under the pressure of natural selection to serve as sharply defined stimuli influencing the social behavior of fellow members of a species." The important point here is not only that the evolution of species-specific behavior patterns serves as stimuli to influence the behavior of other members of the species, but that such stimuli are part of the totality of the interaction system, organism-environment, and constitute at one and the same time the expression and communication of one individual of the species and the milieu of another. In other words, what is expression for one individual is environment for the other and vice versa. This is of particular importance in the human species as we shall see presently, and it is precisely in this way that we conceive of the social matrix that is the mother-child relationship.

This matrix has evolved in the animal hierarchy from highly automatized interactions to increasingly complex and individuated ones which approach conscious awareness. In a charming and instructive book, *Infancy in Animals*, Maurice Burton[12] describes in detail the bond between mother and offspring in various species. The feeding and protection of nestlings by the mother bird and their gaping or crouching responses; the interlocking behavior patterns of the mother kangaroo and her offspring which result in her grooming the pouch and licking a pathway for the newborn to follow in order to reach and grasp the teat within the pouch; the female wood-rat retrieving her young and carrying them back to the nest, allowing them to become attached to her teats, occasionally licking a foot or flank; the infant sloth cradled by its mother's body and clinging to her hair with an arm around her neck—all these are mother-child interactions which operate through a system of communication consisting of signs and signals, thus guaranteeing the survival of the young. The same liaison which existed prenatally between mother and child and which was based on biochemical communication is continued postnatally through psychological, i.e., behavioral communication.

On the animal level, we can scarcely speak of a relationship in terms of devotion or affection between mother and child. The innate patterns operate too automatically, awareness is not yet present or only very dimly, there is no memory with consequent internalization of the outside world except in a very primitive sense. Yet, even at these levels the newborn is not self-sufficient, and the maternal matrix with its assurance of nourishment and protection from the elements and from predators is essential for survival.

From the standpoint of evolution, the carrying out of the interaction between mother and child in the ontogeny of a species, which we have termed social matrix above, is part of the reproductive cycle, expressed in innate species-specific behavior whose form and content are a positive function of the degree of helplessness of the young and the complexity of the neural equipment. This statement is of fundamental importance to the understanding of the human mother-child relationship. For if we believe that there is an evolutionary continuum from primitive to more complex organisms which includes not only anatomical structures and physiological processes but very especially neurophysiological processes and their reflection in behavior, then the reciprocal attachment of the human mother and child is *an evolutionary given* and needs no theories to account for its existence. The meaning of "attachment" will change as the child matures physically and emotionally and his psychic processes become differentiated. But what of its role in the maturation of that psychic apparatus, ego, through which survival is guaranteed? This is a question we would ask and about which we would build theories. But before we undertake to examine in detail the mother-child interaction in *Homo sapiens*, let us see whether studies of the subhuman primates reveal facts which are important to the understanding of man.

Chimpanzees have been observed in their natural habitat by Kortlandt.[13] We should like to quote his concluding remarks because of their particular relevance to ego formation. "All the chimpanzees I observed were cautious, hesitant creatures. This is one of the major impressions one carries away from studying chimpanzees at close range in the wild. Behind their lively, searching eyes one senses a doubting, contemplative personality, always trying to make sense out of a puzzling world. It is as if the *certainty of instinct* has been replaced in chimpanzees by the *uncertainty of intellect*—but without the determination and decisiveness that characterize man."*

What Kortlandt terms intellect heralds the primitive beginnings of ego in the human sense, for it implies that many of the exigencies of life, the disorganizing factors of the environment, are to be met by consciously directed attention, thought, memory of past experiences or situations, communication and interrelation with others, and insightful behavior. All of these psychic processes require synthesis before they can result in action adequate for survival. They must therefore be integrated by some form of rudimentary ego process. This fact is of the utmost importance in the mother-child relationship. It means that ego processes will mediate this interaction: Only some of the mother's reactions to and behavior toward her child (primarily the emotional ones) will be instinctive; the rest will be guided by experience, and the intention of teaching her offspring. The child

---

* Italics ours.

must superimpose learning on instinctive behavior; he must acquire knowledge about the physical environment, the sources of food, the forest terrain and the open ground, and the ways of his social group. Above all, he must integrate his psychic experience so that it becomes available for action; he, too, must structure a rudimentary ego.

All this is the result of the replacement of automatically functioning innate behavior patterns which go into operation at birth by learned behavior which must be acquired by an extremely helpless newborn individual over a considerable period of time. Thus, the chimpanzee, as the human child, is characterized by a long pedamorphic period. Children are carried on the mother's back until they are four. Mothers are extremely cautious and circumspect and avoid exposing their children to any possible risk. Even up to puberty they were seldom let out of sight. Children "always obeyed their mothers at the first hint," and "asked for food by holding out one hand. If a mother and child were seated side by side and the mother wanted to move on, she had only to look at her offspring for it to jump up on her back; if by chance the child was looking the other way, she merely tapped it lightly on the shoulder or arm." Thus do chimpanzees communicate in a mother-child relatedness that is essential for survival and has been guaranteed by evolutionary processes through the child's capacity to learn within a medium in which the nurturing, protective impulses of the mother are fused with her need to teach, i.e., to communicate knowledge and experience however primitive.

That a relatively high degree of individuation, as reflected in child-rearing procedures, is already present in this subhuman primate is illustrated by an interesting observation by Kortlandt. He noted that one mother who was much older than the rest tended to give her children more freedom. Apparently, experience had taught her that the environment was reasonably safe and that she could leave her two children at the edge of the forest while she went to pick papaws in the plantation. Her children were noticeably more self-reliant than other youngsters of approximately the same age. Already we see the influence of the character of the maternal matrix on the rate of maturation, and ultimately on the personality and nature of the ego of the young.

Another carefully detailed observation of subhuman primates is Schaller's[14] work on gorillas in their natural habitat. Here, we find ample confirmation of the close interaction between mother and child. Schaller's experiences of living among gorillas for many months led him to the following conclusions: "The comfort and security which the infant derives from close contact with the female, even after she has ceased to provide food is probably essential to its bodily and mental well-being. This continuous social contact undoubtedly contributes to the infant's later successful integration into the group as a whole. From the age of about two and a half months the infant exhibits a growing awareness of the environment and with it a desire to explore and seek social contact with other group members.* Through the behavior of its mother it probably learns to recognize the meaning of various gestures and the proper response to certain vocalizations, essential knowledge in a closely knit society. . . . The mother is also the only object in the environment of the infant to which it can turn at all times. . . . Females too sought contact with their offspring, seemingly for social reasons alone. . . ."

In the experimental laboratory, Harlow and Zimmerman[15, 16] have conclusively demonstrated the affectional tie of infant monkeys to the mother, and by isolating tactile

---

* We would like to call attention to the self-actualizing nature of such behavior. It would seem to presage the self-actualizing tendencies of the human ego in its search for stimuli upon which to grow and structure itself.

stimuli from food-giving ones in the form of mechanical, surrogate mothers, have shown that physical contact is the critical factor in establishing this bond. It is the terrycloth mother to whom the baby monkey runs, and to whom he clings in a fear-provoking situation, and not the wire mother, although she provides nourishment. It is also in the comforting, tactile, experience of his clinging to the terry-cloth mother that he overcomes his fear, and finds the courage to accede to his curiosity and exploratory urges.

If the social matrix, mother-child, with the subsequent addition of other group members, is so essential to the child-hood development of our primate cousins, how much more so is this the case for the human child whose period of peda-morphy is even longer, whose neural equipment is much more complex and requires a longer time for complete maturation, and whose relationship to all aspects of the environment is complicated by its internalization through symbolic repre-sentations which ultimately find expression in speech.* In the literature of psychoanalysis, which belatedly in its his-tory became concerned with the mother-child relationship, the issue seems to be not whether this relationship is impera-tive for the child's survival, but whether it is primary as "relationship," or has developed secondarily in response to the gratification of physiological needs, such as the need for food, warmth, and protection. Bowlby[18] reviews these varying points of view most ably. Although it is impossible to quote his work extensively within the framework of this book, a few examples will illustrate the divergent opinions.

---

* "The period of infant dependency is one year in monkeys, two years in apes, and six to eight years in modern man."

". . . development of the cerebral part of man's brain is transported into a setting in the external world where it becomes subject to all the parental, familial, and other inter-personal influences of modern man's social environ-ment, as well as to features of his cultural heritage, accumulated during a civilization of several thousand years."[17]

He makes clear the classic Freudian view, espoused as recently as 1954 by Anna Freud,[19] who says: "The relationship to the mother is not the infant's first relationship to the environment. What precedes it is an earlier phase in which not the object world but the body needs and their satisfaction or frustration play the decisive part. . . ." To many workers in the field, this theory was not satisfying and did not correspond to their observations of infants. Thus, Melanie Klein,[20] observing the infant's attentive listening to the mother's voice and responding to it with a facial expression clearly manifesting pleasure, concludes "that gratification is as much related to the object which gives the food as to the food itself." There are references in the work of Ribble, Benedek, and Spitz to the importance of contact in the social bond between mother and child. Yet, none of them give up completely the theory that this is exclusively the product of the meeting of physiological needs. The psychoanalysts of the Hungarian school, influenced by the work of Ferenczi and I. Hermann, have come to a different conclusion. Thus, Michael and Alice Balint conceive of the infant as active in a primitive and primary object relationship with the mother.

The Learning Theorists, like the classical Freudians, hold to a theory of Secondary Drive, assuming that only physiological needs are primary and that they serve as the motivating forces on the basis of which relatedness to others is learned. On the other hand, those psychologists who have made extensive observations of infants, for example Charlotte Buehler, "have been struck by the specificity of the responses babies show to human beings in the first weeks of life: They respond to the human face and voice in a way different from the way they respond to all other stimuli."[18]

Such specificity is reminiscent of the innate behavior patterns characteristic of mother-child interaction in animal species as described by the ethologists. It is indeed this etho-

logical model of interaction which Bowlby himself employs
to convey his conception of the bond between mother and
child. In his view, the human infant is innately equipped with
five instinctual responses which together constitute a pattern
of attachment behavior: sucking, clinging, following, crying,
and smiling. This pattern is activated in the interaction with
the mother and has evolved, as in the young of other species,
to ensure survival. Our point of view regarding the innate-
ness of a patterned response that guarantees mother-child
interaction is in agreement with Bowlby. Such a view eschews
the question of whether such relatedness is based on a primary
object relationship, or arises secondarily in connection with
the gratification of physiological needs; for it looks to the
larger biological framework of evolution for an understanding
of all phenomena associated with species survival. Within such
a framework, there is no straight-line causality, and therefore
no "primary" and "secondary" in the causal sense. There are
patterned processes and interacting totalities, which in the
arena of the evolutionary process become selected out because of their greater adaptive efficacy. This is as true for
the evolution of forms of social interaction and psychic
structure as for the physical substratum that makes this
possible. From an evolutionary standpoint, it is impossible
to say that the child learns to love his mother *because* she
feeds him; one can only say that an organism as complex
and as physically and neurologically immature at birth as
the human child could only be fed within the framework
of a social situation in which many intricate and interacting
behavioral responses on the part of mother and child meet
a multiplicity of developmental needs. Informed with the
evolutionary dimension of socially interacting responses,
Peiper,[21] in a most detailed description of the neurology of
food intake, calls attention to an aspect of the mother's role in
nursing her baby which is seldom realized:

"If the baby is at a distance from his mother's breast he must bring his head nearer to her, for only then can he take the appropriate part of the breast, that is, the nipple, into his mouth. The reflex described above [the rooting reflex] assists him in this task. The effort of the human baby is supported by his mother who takes him to her breast. Her assistance, which today seems so self-evident to us, developed very late phylogenetically. Even among the chimpanzees, which among the anthropoids are most similar to man, the baby gets little help from his mother. . . .

"In mammals which are phylogenetically lower than the apes, the mother is still less helpful to her baby when it searches for the breast."

The phylogeny of certain behavioral aspects of the early interaction of human mother and child is thus clearly documented.

Of paramount importance among developmental needs is that of synthesizing out of the unfolding of such ego functions as perception, physical co-ordinations, cognition, speech, a unified psychic structure, namely ego. It is interesting that whereas Bowlby sees the process of psychic organization developing throughout the early months of the infant's life and attributes to it the function of relating the child to the mother-figure, he believes that his study is confined to the instinctual roots of the child's tie, and does not deal with ego or super-ego processes. It would seem to us that his study goes beyond his own conception of it, and that in fact it is impossible to separate so-called instinctual roots from roots of ego processes. What we actually witness in the human child is the maturation of neurophysiological processes which are reflected in a gradually awakening awareness. Thus, the very instinctual response pattern which Bowlby describes—sucking, clinging, following, crying, and smiling—will have different meanings at different levels of awareness, and will become incorporated into ego structure with meanings, i.e., internalized psychic images that correspond to advancing levels of ego maturation.* The operation of the instinctual response system and ego are interlocking processes and the manner of their mutual interaction within the framework of the mother-child relationship, with its specific character and coloration, will determine the quality of ego in a particular individual.

Thus far, our attention has been directed primarily toward the child and the native endowments which enable him to use the social matrix in the maturation of his ego. What of the mother? What crucial factors does she bring to the relationship? These are the instinctual impulses to feed, cradle, stroke, protect, smile at, play with, and talk to her baby which dovetail with and are reinforced by the instinctual response pattern of the child. But unlike the infant, these maternal responses are operative within a framework of the most highly organized awareness. It is the fusion of this awareness of all aspects of the maternal experience—from pregnancy, through the birth, nursing, and rearing of the child—with the affectional response system which we have just described, that constitutes the beginnings of love and causes the mother to place the survival of the child above her own. Obviously, there will be great individual differences in the acuity of awareness and the extent and vitality of the affectional reactions. Whatever the particular individual nature of the maternal personality, however, it forms the medium for the child out of which, through reciprocal interaction, the maturation of nervous system and the ontogenous development of the ego proceed.

As mentioned above, physical contact with the mother, or mother surrogate, is essential to the normal development of

---

* Schilder expresses a similar view: "I consider grasping, groping, and sucking to be the nucleus of the function of the ego and the ego instincts."[22]

the infant's nervous system.[23] How is such contact transformed into the further growth of nervous tissue, as in the case of myelinization, for example? The hypothesis suggests itself in very general terms: The afferent impulses set off by the skin contact are transformed through central nervous system intervention to efferent responses leading to sources of endocrine, hormonal products that promote growth of nervous tissue as well as to that state of emotional equilibrium necessary for such growth. We might consider this process the reverse of the one described by Cannon [24] in which strong emotions such as rage and fear produce bodily and endocrine changes of the nature of the "stress" [25] syndrome, whereas the tactile contact in the affectional interaction between mother and child sets in motion physiochemical processes conducive to the calming of strong emotions, such as anxiety, as well as creating the systemic conditions necessary for the maturation of nervous tissue. This is a clear point at which the mother's life-giving function on the purely physical level includes much more than the giving of food.

The integrative ego processes which must of necessity go on within the mother as a consequence of her experience of having a child have an important bearing on the development of the child's ego. In this social interaction system on which the survival of the species depends, it is she alone for whom at the beginning awareness is available, to be implemented in the interests of the child's psychological maturation, i.e., primarily in the structuring of his ego. This process begins for the mother with the integration of a new body image which gradually becomes associated with her child. She is aware of the cessation of menstruation, of the first fetal movements, and of the steady increase in abdominal size and tension. When pregnancy ends, the mother realizes that the newborn infant is associated with these processes and is related to her in the profound sense of being separate but physically dependent on her, and that a history of relatedness links them together. We regard this as the starting point of human social relations. It combines instinctual maternal responses* with conscious experiential elements. It is the mother's conscious awareness of the physical, psychological, and emotional relationship between herself and her child that is the new and characteristically human aspect of the social matrix. The knowledge that the child is a part of herself, and yet separate, that the long period of childhood dependency will involve them in reciprocal interaction for some time, together with the conscious perception of the child and pleasure in his growth, and the response to his needs which includes the awareness of her response—all of these lay the groundwork for the internalization in the mother's mind of an image of her child. It should perhaps be made clear that in the realm of mother-child interaction much takes place on an intuitive basis which is an admixture of instinctual response with half-conscious awareness. The terms knowledge or consciousness do not necessarily imply an actively directed awareness, rather a psychological process which is the opposite of automatic, and which carries with it a highly individuated coloration stemming from the inherent psychophysical nature, as well as the emotional, intellectual, and social history of the mother. It is the laying down and synthesizing of a pattern of impressions which constitute the conception of her child and the integration of this image with memories of her own childhood (affectional memories of being mothered as well as cognitive ones of her mother's image of her) that make possible the mother's empathic discernment of the needs and nature of her child. The constellation of attitudes, affects, and behavioral responses which are an outgrowth of

---

* Tinbergen[26] refers to a parental instinct, quoting Lorenz, and cites certain physical properties of the child as the releasers for these responses. Rensch[27] posits maternal instinct.

this empathic discernment, we call the act of loving. For the human mother then, because of consciousness and memory, this act takes place through the superimposition on instinctual responses of complex ego integrative processes. The mother perceives and reacts not only to the objective needs and developmental level of the child, but also "reads into" his behavior meanings which stem from her own need for social contact and communication with him. It is the mutuality of need that creates the environment in which the child can learn and grow and that fosters the development of his ego.

A very instructive example of this process and some apt comments regarding it are given by Escalona[28] in a discussion with educators and research workers in the field of child development. She remarks that mothers often ask whether the smile-like grimace which they observe in their two-day-old infants actually signifies a recognition of them as a special mother-person or not. Although the obvious objective fact is that a perception of this sort is impossible at that early developmental level, Escalona feels that the "truth" of this fact should be sacrificed for a larger and more meaningful one. She says: "It is my firm conviction that every mother should be encouraged to believe that at age two days the grimace is a smile, because I think the baby learns to smile as an act of recognition, by being responded to as though he already were smiling . . . all sorts of involuntary, or at least wholly unstructured movements of face or body become meaningful symbols of communication largely because they are misinterpreted as such by proud mothers." The importance of Escalona's remark lies obviously not in her wish to misinform mothers—a point not to be taken too literally—but in her profound understanding of the empathic interaction system "mother-child," and its importance to the growth of the child. The innate mechanisms unfold more rapidly and felicitously and the development of the learned responses is facilitated if these processes take place in a maternal matrix which anticipates them affirmatively. It is this empathic identification which acts as a stimulus for the continuing development of the child's ego.*

Developmental studies of childhood as they deal with the unfolding of innate capacities and potentialities had previously been characterized almost exclusively by observations of the child from the beginning of life. More recently, such studies (by, e.g., A. Balint; Bowlby; Spitz; Wolf; Fries; Ribble; Brody; Escalona), inspired by the awareness of the importance of the emotional relationship between mother and child which psychoanalysis brought into the field have taken this interaction into account. An evolutionary approach to the study of childhood, with special emphasis on the ontogeny of ego, however, would require that we add to our view of this development within the framework of mother-child interaction, a concern with psychological processes within the mother since she represents the child's first environment. What is of primary importance in this interaction is the mother's mental image of the child—an image that grows out of the mother's need to nurture and love her child and that is being continuously shaped and reshaped as the mother responds to developmental processes within the child. It is this image with its variegated coloration which is reflected back to the child in all that the mother communicates to him, in gesture, action, and word, and which forms the background for the qualitative character of his ego.

By what processes is the child enabled to make use of these communications? How are they incorporated into and how do they promote the growth of his own ego? Let us reach

---

* "Although the object relation is a necessary prerequisite for identification, identification is an independent biological attitude, indicating the social character of living beings and their experiences."[22]

far back to a theory of the origins of life for an analogy that may clarify the process. When increasingly complex protein molecules become transformed from inorganic substances to living ones, it could be hypothesized that in the struggle for sources of energy which ensued those molecules survived as living which developed the self-catalyzing ability to effect this change without the intervention of an external catalyst. Thus, catalyst A accelerates the transformation of substance B (nonliving molecule) to substance C (living molecule). If, however, substance C is a self-catalyzing agent for the reaction B transformed into C, then it can itself convert B into C, thus gaining an evolutionary advantage in time, and therefore in the quantity of such transformations, over substances which need a catalyst external to themselves.[29] The ability of the human nervous system to convert external impressions into psychic entities, which in turn are used to build psychic structures, is reminiscent of a self-catalyzing reaction. The nervous system of the child (substance C) has the capacity to convert perceptions, experiences of interaction and communication with the mother (substance B) into itself, i.e., to give psychological life to itself by transforming the outside world into a part of its own ego. This is accomplished through the introjection of these experiences, which means that memory traces laid down by them become integrated into a patterned whole which is the ego. It is the ability to introject, to fix the outer world within the human organism in a permanent, unified, yet flexible and individuated way, which reveals the endogenous growth potential and self-actualizing aspect of ego function as it operates from its most rudimentary beginnings and itself continues to build more and more upon itself.

For the child, introjection is the vehicle to imitation and ultimately to identification. There are in the course of maturation patterns of self-imitation in which the objectified perception and awareness by the baby of his own movements are introjected, internalized, i.e., remembered and repeated. This process is beautifully described by Buehler.[30] When the remembered movement is repeated, it has become integrated into the rudimentary ego. Analogous but infinitely more complex processes of introjection and imitation take place in the infant's interaction with his mother. The entire constellation of the mother's emotional attitudes, as revealed in her gestures, bodily movements, voice quality, and smile, are apprehended by the child even before the development of speech and are introjected by him, so that they ultimately form part of the core of his own ego. These introjections occur unconsciously and the innate capacity to effect them could perhaps be thought of as a primitive learning process which serves the same function as do the inherent behavior patterns of animals.

These subtle processes of introjection in which maternal attitudes and modes are incorporated, which may later in life have a profound effect on the individual's self-conception, on his sexual identity, or his affectional capacities and the mood in which he views the world, go hand in hand with the species' characteristic maturation of bodily functions, speech, intellect, and cognitive processes. In the area of the development of speech, the introjection and imitation of maternal "style" becomes very apparent. For example, the children of foreign-born parents, although exposed to other individuals who speak the native language without accent, will clearly imitate the "foreign accent" of their mothers in their early years. Penfield[31] confirms this in his discussion of the brain-mechanisms of language. Because the early acquisition of language presents us with such an excellent illustration of the co-ordinated interaction of inherited mechanisms with processes of learning—the capacity for which is given—operating in the affectional and cognitive matrix of mother-child interchange, it is rewarding to quote Penfield in some detail.

> During normal speech it may be said that two mechanisms are employed, and both are present only in the human brain. There is an ideational mechanism which makes available the acquired elements of speech, and a motor articulation mechanism that is inborn but may be utilized by the voluntary motor system.
>
> The ideational part of speech, whether spoken, heard, written, or read, depends upon the employment of a certain portion of one hemisphere alone—normally the left hemisphere. This localization of a function in one hemisphere is, in itself, something new in mammalian evolution. Other intellectual functions, such as perception, the recording of current experiences, and the storing of generalizations or concepts in memory, are made possible by the utilization of homologous areas of cerebral cortex on the two sides, together with the coordinating and integrating work of the higher brain stem.
>
> It is thanks to the action of the ideational speech areas of the dominant cortex, and their connections with a small zone of gray matter below the cortex in the thalamus, that words may be "found" by the individual.

We would like at this point to introduce the psychological element at work in this process, i.e., the integrative function of ego, for it is ego in the individual that enables him to "find" the word, to set in motion and synthesize the action of the brain areas involved in speech which Penfield mentions.

Regarding the learning of language, Penfield stresses the importance of conforming such learning to the changing capacities of the child's brain, and points out that the direct learning of language by the "mother's method," whether for one or for a number of secondary languages, is the most felicitous. His description of this process is a beautiful example of the reciprocal interaction between mother and child (which in our view is the result of evolutionary processes), with its content of interest, affection, emotional empathic discernment, and appreciation on the part of the mother, and ego-expansive eagerness to learn, to communicate, and to master reality on the part of the child.

The mother's method is simple. It is familiar to everyone. Nevertheless, let us examine it. Even before the child understands, the mother talks to him. Before he speaks she watches for understanding. When he says his first words he has a delighted audience.* Language is for him only a means to an end, never an end in itself. When he learns about words he is learning about life, learning to get what he wants, learning to share his own exciting ideas with others, learning to understand wonderful fairy tales and exciting facts about trains and trucks and animals and dolls. One secret of the success of this method is, of course, that it is employed while a child is forming the speech units in his eager little brain.

It is clear that Penfield fully appreciates the importance of the social matrix and its specific ingredient of maternal love in the development and maturation of the species-specific behavior: speech. What is left unclear is the process by which neurophysiological capacity, having reached the necessary maturational level, is transformed into words which are spoken in the mother's intonation and accent. There is a hint in a few short sentences of processes such as we have posited: "It is difficult to make any certain statement on the question of accents by reference to the physiological evidence alone. One may say that children have a greater capacity for imitation than adults. That seems to be a fact, but it is not an explanation of what happens in later life."

It is not entirely clear to which later happenings Penfield refers. What is important from our point of view is that at an extremely early age the child's rudimentary ego is able to imitate, i.e., to convert remembered perceptions into ideational and motor patterns of behavior which bear a

---

* This corresponds to the affirmative anticipation described above in connection with the smiling response.

resemblance to the model given by the original percept. The mother in all the details of her behavior and attitude is the first model for such imitation. At a later point, the child's ego unconsciously synthesizes all the imitated details with cognitive experiences and emotional perceptions of the mother into a unified image of the mother which, as an object of identification, constitutes an important part of his own ego.

In view of the development of inherent neurophysiological processes which form the substratum of ego functions, and the active and spontaneous affinity of ego, in the course of development, to its first model and its search for substitute or additional models if the mother should prove inadequate (a phenomenon which we encounter in psychotherapy), it seems difficult to understand a view of the development of psychic structures, the ego among them, as arising predominantly out of the deprivation of instinctual drive needs. Yet, such is the view of classical Freudian thinking as stated by Hartmann, Kris, and Loewenstein.[32] Although granting that "there is an undifferentiated phase in early infancy during which there is maturation of apparatuses that later will come under the control of the ego, and that serve mobility, perception and certain thought processes," these authors see the essential differentiation of the child's ego as based upon his "ability . . . to distinguish between his self and the world around him. The ability to make this distinction depends on the proportion of indulgence to deprivation in the meeting of the child's instinctual needs—largely the need for nourishment." Freud assumed that as long as all needs are gratified, i.e., under "total" indulgence, the infant tends to experience the source of satisfaction as part of the self; partial deprivation thus is probably an essential condition of the infant's ability to distinguish between the self and the object. It "is a necessary, but clearly not a sufficient condition for the establishment of the distinction between the self and the object. The process of distinguishing has a cognitive or perceptual side; it is thus dependent on the maturation of the child's perceptual equipment."

If admittedly the ability to distinguish self from objects is dependent on maturational processes, why is deprivation of instinctual gratification essential at all?

The fallacy seems to stem from the need to account for all psychological phenomena in the tension-reduction terms of a drive theory. The assumption follows then that deprivation, which represents tension, will in some sense as an experience come closer to awareness than the state of reduced tension, namely gratification. In such a theory, it is always the negative aspect of psychic experience, either deprivation or conflict, which becomes the motivating principle of awareness or action. But the human organism needs no gadfly to achieve awareness. What it has achieved phylogenetically through evolution must come to fruition and operate actively in the ontogeny of the individual given the necessary and appropriate environment. This environment will be positively not negatively related to the developmental needs of the organism. The observations of children confirm this. That maternal deprivation has been found to be deleterious to the development of the nervous system and consequently to the maturation of physical and mental functions attests to the fact that the development of psychic structures responds to the positive ministrations of the mother, i.e., to her love.

We would argue further that the structuring of ego in the human infant can neither be the result of the vicissitude of any partial function of the organism, whether instinctual, perceptual, or cognitive processes, or processes of identification* nor of the summative effect of these entities. It is rather

---

* White[83] takes a similar position in regard to identification, pointing out the fact that the infant is equipped "from the start with the kind of energy and with a kind of structure that disposes him to construct a stable, ob-

the outcome of the interaction of all of these developmental processes within the organism as they in turn interact with their first environment, the mother.

Although the relationship between mother and child is for obvious biological reasons the first social interaction, it would be completely inaccurate to regard the structuring of the child's ego as exclusively a product of identifications with her. While the family has varying forms in different cultures and in different historical periods, its general evolutionary development would seem to tend toward greater stability, so that the child experiences consistent contact and meaningful relatedness with other individuals who may also become objects for identification, and therefore of incorporation into ego structures. For the child, the father is a most significant figure in this respect. For him, the experience of parenthood, even the awareness of his role in creating the child, must appear relatively late in hominid evolution. In the subhuman primates, there seems to be no clear indication of a family unit in which male and female continue to live together monogamously and participate jointly in the care of children. Kortlandt describes the social structure among chimpanzees as divided into two loosely knit groups of fifteen or twenty individuals whose character was determined by whether the individuals were childless or child-rearing. Among primitive peoples existing today, the role of the father in impregnating the mother is sometimes not known, as in the case of the Trobrianders. However, with the evolution of greater understanding of the world of reality and of greater relatedness between the sexes, the human family came into existence as a relatively stable social institution.

---

jective, real world." Furthermore, he emphasizes the fact that the capacity to identify with the whole person, as for example the mother, would presuppose the capacity in developmental terms, to conceive of a totality—a capacity which must depend on a neurophysiological level of maturation.

The maternal role still centered around the care of the young; the paternal role on the conquest of the physical world in terms of providing food, shelter, and protection for the family group. Regardless of the level of sociocultural evolution, for almost all societies, something of this fundamental difference in orientation to the world, and therefore in ego mode, will exist between male and female. The mother, whose task is nurturing, will be focused on empathic identification, the better to give what is needed; the father's ego structure is organized in the direction of exploitation of the physical and social environment: controlling, changing, shaping it in the service of survival. For the primitive male, the hunting of prey and the maintenance of security against the dangers of environment left little room for identification with "the other." In fact, such an orientation might lead to a failure to survive. To some extent then, the capacity of the male child to identify with a mother, which was necessary for his early learning in the maternal matrix, had, in the name of the ability to survive competently in the physical world, to be turned into "disidentifications." Something of these basic differences still persist, although they change considerably as a result of shifts in social and economic structure. We shall deal with the processes of identification and disidentification in greater detail and as they apply to social processes later, when we come to consider questions of ethical evolution.

As the child's ever widening awareness and comprehension gives him an increasingly accurate conception of the nature of his social milieu, he forms an affectional bond with the father, and identifies with him. In forming his own ego-identity, it is normally the boy who identifies more strongly with the father, the girl with the mother—an intricate and specialized aspect of ego-structuring as it relates to sexual identity.

We cannot leave the question of the formation of ego without touching upon the problem of socialization. Demands, expectations, prohibitions are part of the child's earliest experience with his mother. These are introjected as stemming from her, in the same way as are the words of his mother-tongue, and behavior appropriate to them becomes associated with the gestures, words, and the emotional tone in which they are expressed. We do not believe that it is exclusively the fear of the loss of the mother's love that accounts for his acceding to her demands; but is more fundamentally predicated on the experience of having been loved by her, which includes his unconscious or foreconscious perception of her wish that he develop optimal ego function and social adaptedness appropriate to his phase of development.[34] This results in his identification with her wishes. The early incorporation of the mother's demands and expectations on the basis of a primarily empathic relationship paves the way for the child's acceptance of commandments and prohibitions which he acquires in his identification with the less empathic, generally more authoritarian figure, the father. This incorporation of commandments corresponds roughly to Fromm's conception of the "authoritarian conscience"[35] and differs from Freud's conception of the origin of the super-ego[36] in the sense that it is derived *directly* from the ego function of identification and is not conceived as having been precipitated primarily as a result of instinctual frustration (Oedipal strivings). Thus, the roots of conscience are laid down and the most social of creatures begins to become socialized, i.e., to adapt to the requirements of the culture in which he is being reared. But socialization is far more than mere compliance with prohibitions and demands. It includes an integration into the functioning ego—again initially through identifications with parents—of the positive social acquisitions of a culture, first as individually represented by the parents, and subsequently by the broadening social encounters of the growing child. Language, religion, moral and ethical codes, interpersonal value systems thus become part of the child's ego and together with his native predispositions determine the nature of his human encounters. It is important to remember that whereas the content of individual experiences which ultimately eventuate in identifications may be consciously remembered, the actual processes of introjection and identification take place on an unconscious level. Of the most significant things which parents communicate on this level are their strivings, aspirations, and image of what they would wish their child to be or become. Earlier, we mentioned that the mother's mental image of her child is communicated to him. As the child grows, the father's image of the child is added to the mother's; the content of the image, even though it is also largely unconscious for the parents, becomes more structured, and the child's capacities for perceiving it, for responding to it, grow more sensitive as awareness is heightened. This syndrome of projected aspirations which the child incorporates and synthesizes into his ego and which form the nucleus of his ego-ideal have an important bearing on sociocultural evolution. To the extent that they reflect the value systems of the culture in question, they are the stabilizing influence; through them, the child absorbs the traditions of his society and his ego becomes a part of it. If the parental strivings for the child go beyond the established framework of their society, and the child identifies positively with these strivings, he may become in some sense the unusual or exceptional individual who is the instrument for evolutionary advance in the psychosocial sense. However, there are also retrogressive aspects to such identification processes. The child sometimes identifies with the repressed, unconscious, anti-social impulses of the parents, and the result is a delinquent or criminal personality.[37]

While the kernel of the child's value system as it becomes part of his ego-ideal is established through identifications with parental figures, its more final form is the result of the ego capacity to select, seek out, and synthesize out of the totality of his social encounter and experience with the environment those elements which are most congenial to his inherent nature and capability, more in harmony with his core ego-ideal, and to structure them into a unit which will play a major role in determining his thought and action. It is the uniqueness of this ego-ideal and the extent of the opportunity which a given society presents for its implementation, which together form a major vehicle for sociocultural advance.

It is interesting that the differentiation and structuring of that very part of ego on which an important aspect of an individual's socialization depends, namely the ego-ideal, can itself become the means by which society becomes increasingly socialized, i.e., advances to new levels of human interaction. We shall discuss this more fully in our chapter on ethics.

In summary, we may say that in the affectional-cognitive matrix of interaction between mother and child, the step is made from awareness as a perceptual phenomenon to internalization by rudimentary ego functions of what is perceived through processes of imitation, introjection, and identification. These internalized symbolic representations of "the other," the "love-object," become part of the child's ego. Ego-formation, a process necessary for human survival, is thus inevitably bound to the experience of being loved and is the concomitant of the long pedamorphic period of childhood. The characteristic human interdependence of the growth of psychic structures and emotional relatedness within a social matrix is in itself a product of evolution, namely, the evolution of the nervous system with its specifically human capacity for memory, speech, symbolization, conceptualization, and abstract thinking. Ego processes synthesize out of a variety and complexity of experience a differentiated aspect of ego: the ego-ideal. Sociocultural evolution is then served by the improvement of autonomous ego functions and by the changing and advancing content of new ego-ideals, as these are created by unique individuals, in a social setting which gives them opportunity for self-realization.

■ REFERENCES

1. Gerard, R.: Becoming—the residue of change. In Tax, S., Ed.: *The Evolution of Man, Evolution After Darwin*, Vol. II. University of Chicago Press, Chicago, 1960, pp. 263, 264.
2. Bullock, T. H.: Evolution of neurophysiological mechanisms. In Roe, A., and Simpson, G. G., Eds.: *Behavior and Evolution*. Yale University Press, New Haven, 1958, pp. 165-177.
3. Washburn, S. L., and Avis., V.: Evolution of human behavior. In Roe, A., and Simpson, G. G., Eds.: *Behavior and Evolution*. Yale University Press, New Haven, 1958, pp. 421-436.
4. Erikson, E. H.: *Identity and the Life Cycle*. International Universities Press, New York, 1959, p. 52.
5. Spitz, R.: Hospitalism. *The Psychoanalytic Study of the Child*, Vol. I. International Universities Press, New York, 1945.
6. Seitz, P. F. D.: Infantile experience and adult behavior in animal subjects. *Psychosomatic Medicine 21:* 353-378, 1959.
7. Beach, F. A., and Jaynes, J.: Effects of early experience upon the behavior of animals. *Psychological Bulletin 51:* May, 1954.
8. Harlow, H. F.: The heterosexual affectional system in monkeys. *American Psychologist 17:* 1-9, 1962.

9. Denenberg, V. H., and Bell, R. W.: Critical periods for the effects of infantile experience on adult learning. *Science 131:* 22, 1960.

10. Lorenz, K.: Companionship in bird life (1935). In Schiller, C. H., Ed.: *Instinctive Behavior.* International Universities Press, New York, 1957.

11. Lorenz, K.: The evolution of behavior. *Scientific American,* December, 1958, p. 6.

12. Burton, M.: *Infancy in Animals.* Hutchinson, London, 1956.

13. Kortlandt, A.: Chimpanzees in the wild. *Scientific American,* May, 1962, Vol. 1206, No. 5.

14. Schaller, G. B.: *The Mountain Gorilla.* University of Chicago Press, Chicago, 1963.

15. Harlow, H. F., and Zimmerman, R. R.: Affectional responses in the infant monkey. *Science 130:*421-432, 1959.

16. Harlow, H. F.: Love in infant monkeys. *Scientific American,* June, 1959.

17. Magoun, H. W., Darling, L., and Prost, J.: The evolution of man's brain. In Brazier, M. A. B., Ed.: *The Central Nervous System and Behavior.* Josiah Macy, Jr., Foundation and National Science Foundation, New York, 1960.

18. Bowlby, J.: The nature of the child's tie to his mother. *International Journal of Psychiatry XXXIX:* 1-24, 1959.

19. Freud, A.: Psychoanalysis and education. In *The Psychoanalytic Study of the Child.* International Universities Press, New York, IX, 1954.

20. Klein, M.: *Envy and Gratitude.* Basic Books, New York, 1957.

21. Peiper, A.: *Cerebral Function in Infancy and Childhood.* Consultants' Bureau, New York, 1963, p. 410.

22. Schilder, P.: *Mind, Perception and Thought.* Columbia University Press, New York, 1942, pp. 240, 251.

23. Thompson, W. R., and Schaeffer, T., Jr.: Early environmental stimulation. In Fiske, D. W., and Maddi, S. R., Eds.: *Functions of Varied Experience.* Dorsey Press, Homewood, Ill., 1961, Ch. 4.

24. Cannon, W. B.: *Bodily Changes in Pain, Hunger, Fear and Rage.* Branford, Boston, 1929.

25. Selye, H.: *The Stress of Life*. McGraw-Hill, New York, 1956.
26. Tinbergen, N.: *The Study of Instinct*. Clarendon Press, Oxford, 1958, pp. 208-209.
27. Dobzhansky, T.: *Mankind Evolving*. Yale University Press, New Haven, 1962, p. 205.
28. Escalona, S.: Emotional development in the first year of life. *Problems of Infancy and Childhood*. Transactions of the 6th Conference, Mar. 17 and 18, Josiah Macy, Jr., Foundation, New York, 1952.
29. Rush, J. H.: *The Dawn of Life*. Signet, New York, 1957, pp. 151-152.
30. Buehler, C.: *Kindheit und Jugend*. S. Hirzel, Leipzig, 1931.
31. Penfield, W., and Roberts, L.: *Speech and Brain-Mechanisms*. Princeton University Press, Princeton, N. J., 1959, pp. 249, 253, 254.
32. Hartmann, H., Kris, E., and Loewenstein, R. M.: Comments on the formation of psychic structure. *The Psychoanalytic Study of the Child*, Vol. II. International Universities Press, New York, 1946.
33. White, R. W.: *Ego and Reality in Psychoanalytic Theory*. International Universities Press, New York, 1963, pp. 60, 105.
34. Russell, C., and Russell, W. M. S.: *Human Behavior*. Little, Brown, Boston, 1961, p. 147.
35. Fromm, E.: *Man for Himself*. Rinehart, New York, 1947, p. 143.
36. Freud, S.: The passing of the Oedipus complex. *Collected Papers*, Vol. II. Hogarth Press, London, 1953, pp. 269-282.
37. Johnson, A. M., and Szurek, S. A.: The genesis of anti-social acting out in children and adults. *Psychoanalytic Quarterly* XXI: 323-343, 1952.

10 · ANXIETY AND GUILT

In the world of living things, fear is the handmaiden of survival. To human eyes, it usually appears as an unwelcome by-product of the interaction of organism and environment. Yet, as an affective experience, fear has evolved from the dim unknowingness of the primitive organism's withdrawal from stimuli that threaten life through the entire range of awareness to its final manifestation in man, where memory and consciousness may cause it to become transformed into anxiety.

Much has been written about fear in an attempt to understand its manifestations and its causes, and to distinguish it from anxiety. For centuries it had been the concern of philosophers, and more recently of psychologists, neurophysiologists, psychoanalysts, and psychotherapists. One is impressed by the mixture of validity and limitation which our accumulated knowledge and theory of fear and anxiety present. Each hypothesis, each piece of experimental evidence, illuminates a specific aspect of the problem, yet the creation of a cohesive theory into which the valid explanations of partial phenomena can fit remains elusive. There is a variety of reasons for this. One lies in the very nature of affect or emotion itself, of which fear and anxiety are examples. Affects are "par excellence" psychological phenomena, and as such share with reactivity, movement, intention behavior, and thought the duality of a neurophysiological substratum and a mental aspect. That affects are both consequences of and factors in the continuous, ongoing interaction of organism and environment, both internal and external, further complicates this duality. In relation to their psychophysical nature, they are also both cause and effect. Moreover, since the hierarchical increase of awareness in the evolutionary process changes the nature and function of affect by adding, in varying degrees, a subjective element, the investigation of affective responses has been limited understandably to some special dimension of such manifestations. This has certainly been the case in the study of fear and anxiety.

Before we proceed with some examples of observations and theories arrived at in regard to fear and anxiety, let us make a general distinction between them which will apply throughout our discussion and which in its broad outlines finds acceptance among most psychologists. Although reactions akin to anxiety, such as timidity, apprehension, and suspicion, have been observed in animals, anxiety proper is considered a human manifestation. Freedman and Roe[1] say that "the age of anxiety" may properly be said to have started with the emergence of *Homo sapiens*. This is because anxiety is an anticipatory phenomenon in awareness in which clues from the external environment or from the inner state of the human organism serve as signals of danger by touching off, through associative links, previously experienced states of fearfulness, pain, or displeasure. The capacity for storing experience in the form of symbolic memory traces and reawakening them through associative processes gives man the ability to experience anxiety and to heed its warning of danger by taking appropriate action. This capacity is obviously the product of the evolution of man's higher cortical centers which resulted in consciousness and the ability to internalize the environment through its symbolic representation. However, we do not wish to imply that all of human anxiety is dependent on verbal conceptualizations and their memory traces. We are familiar with anxiety which has its origin in a preverbal period of ontogenetic development; nor are we unaware that anxiety may be unconscious, especially in its more neurotic forms. Nevertheless, the characteristically human aspect of anxiety viewed psychobiologically is its existence in conscious experience and its anticipatory function.

By its very nature, anxiety is diffuse, for it is an emotion touched off by a constellation of stimuli acting on an inner, central configuration which consists of many associative pathways. Fear, on the other hand, is more focused on a specific object or situation, and although its appearance may be influenced by the past history of an individual organism, it is generally regarded as a more immediate reaction to the dangers implicit in a presenting stimulus. One might almost say that anxiety, by virtue of its anticipatory nature, could be called a "state," whereas fear could be termed a "reaction." For man, fear is a part of conscious experience; for his evolutionary ancestors, it is manifested in psychophysical reactions, from which we deduce the emotion "fear." Thus, Darwin[2] wrote: "The fact that the lower animals are excited by the same emotions as ourselves is so well established that it will not be necessary to weary the reader by many details. Terror acts in the same manner on them as on us, causing the muscles to tremble, the heart to palpitate, the sphincters to be relaxed and the hair to stand on end. Suspicion, the offspring of fear, is eminently characteristic of most wild animals."

For our evolutionary concerns, the important fact is that fear is a universal response of living tissue, whether manifested in the simple avoidance response of the stentor when an irritant is introduced into its environment or transformed through the evolution of the higher brain centers into a consciously experienced awareness of anxiety in man. One of its main functions is to call forth from the organism that appropriate behavioral response which will eliminate the threat to survival which the environment has presented, and reinstate the organism's optimal interaction with it.

The recognition that the fear-anxiety response is a reaction to a threat to survival in some sense is the common denominator of many theories of anxiety. These derive their conceptions from a concern with man, and are well summarized by Rollo May.[3] For example, Tillich describes anxiety as man's fear of nonbeing or nothingness. Kierkegaard, for whom the goal of personality development is freedom, by which he meant the realization of his creative expansiveness, saw anxiety as inevitably present when the actualization of such possibility was at hand. Expressed in modern psychobiological terms, Kierkegaard's concept points to the factor of disturbance in homeostasis, to instability or transition in a psychological state as the element threatening the integrity of the individual, and therefore his psychological survival.

According to Kurt Goldstein,[4] an organism is thrown into a catastrophic condition when it cannot cope with the demands of its environment; it therefore feels a threat to its existence. The subjective experience of this catastrophic condition is anxiety.

Freud,[5] in dealing with the question of the origins of anxiety, saw it as innate in the organism, part of the self-preservative instinct, and phylogenetically inherited. The large body of his theory of anxiety is concerned with establishing its relationship to the neurotic symptom and with finding a prototype in early ontogenetic development for its later appearance. It would be a digression from the purposes of this study to deal with the details and complexities of Freudian anxiety theory. That Freud attributes anxiety to the self-preservative instinct indicates that he saw it in relationship to danger and survival, both physical and psychological. However, he was limited by the framework within which he sought to study the phenomenon—namely, in its relationship to psychopathology, to the so-called instinctual drives, and to varying states of human consciousness. It was as if the discovery that "hysterics suffered from memories" colored much of Freud's later thinking. Anxiety had also to be understood in terms of specific memories. This led Freud to set up prototypes for anxiety, such as the danger of castration or of the birth experience.

It is true that with the increasing capacity of nervous tissue to store experience as we ascend the evolutionary scale, the factor of historical development will play an ever greater role in the manifestations of the anxiety experience, so that no new threat or danger is experienced without reference to a past—a fact which we discussed above when distinguishing anxiety from fear. However, the diffuse influence of a patterning of experience upon anxiety is quite different from a specific prototype such as Freud attempted to set up.

Other psychoanalysts who deviated from Freud, nevertheless, also sought the answer to the problem of anxiety in terms of the repetition of some fundamental human dilemma which served as a model for all anxiety. Thus for Rank, the experience of separation, exemplified first in the birth trauma, especially as it subsequently implied individuation in the course of human development, was the great danger and threat to which the individual reacted with anxiety.* For Horney, anxiety was a reaction to the disruption of any pattern developed by an individual to ensure his safety: in other words, a reaction to any threat to a defensive system. In Sullivan's[3] eyes, the meaning of anxiety lay in its social aspects, i.e., in "the infant's apprehension of the disapproval of the significant persons in his interpersonal world."

Certainly, all of these views contain some truth. They are in fact statements of various dangers to which the organism, man, does indeed react with anxiety. However, the reaction to danger, whether immediate or anticipated, is not simply a human phenomenon, but a universal reaction of living organisms. It would seem to follow, therefore, that if we were to approach the search for the broadest possible meaning of fear and anxiety within an evolutionary framework, we would find a common denominator under which man's various anxieties could be subsumed.

Earlier in this book we described the evolution of life as a process advancing in time, characterized by an increasing complexity and differentiation of organisms as they interact

---

* Jessie Taft has expressed Rank's conception of anxiety and has carried its meaning beyond the prototype of the birth trauma fully into the realm of the psychological. ". . . Fear is inherent in individuation and self-consciousness in the necessity to be both part and whole . . . always, at bottom, every serious blocking in a human life is the expression of an unsolved or rather unaccepted conflict between the will to become more and more individualized, to develop one's own quantum of life, and the reluctance to pursue wholeheartedly a course which is beyond control by the individual will and which inevitably leads to the annihilation of this dearly bought individuality."[6]

with environment, and calling, therefore, for an increase in the organizational and integrative functions of such organisms. Such a process is antithetical to the increasing disorganizational tendency in the universe as a whole, as implied in the second law of thermodynamics. Unlike the inanimate world, the tendency of the living world, as expressed in the ontogeny and phylogeny of organisms, is toward the creation, maintenance, and further evolution of organized, integrated functioning wholes. One could postulate that fear or anxiety makes its appearance whenever this organizational process is disrupted, in a manner appropriate to the hierarchical level of the neurophysiological processes of the organisms in the evolutionary scale. Thus, fear and anxiety emerge as the inevitable products of the evolutionary process.

Hebb[7] has brought confirmatory evidence for this hypothesis. In his experimental studies of chimpanzees, he elicited avoidance and withdrawal behavior by presenting them with stimuli which varied by some discrepancy from the pattern to which they were accustomed. For example, a detached human face or head, or the lack of responsiveness in a whole animal which was anesthetized, produced marked fear reactions. Thus, Hebb concludes: ". . . fear occurs when an object is seen which is like familiar objects in enough respects to arouse habitual processes of perception, but in other respects arouses incompatible processes."

We must conclude, as does Hebb, that there are centrally organizing and organized processes which have produced *patternings* in the cerebral cortex, and that the disruption of these organizations through the introduction of an incongruous stimulus, for example, will produce fear. Hebb also mentions other disorganizing factors, such as sensory deficit or constitutional change.

In the course of developmental processes in the ontogeny of the human being, similar anxiety can be perceived when a transition occurs from one level of organizational pattern to another on a more advanced level.* Thus, Escalona[8] reports from her observations of infants: ". . . it has seemed to me that so-called eight month's anxiety is a consequence of that step forward in the comprehension of the world about, which enables the baby to perceive that the mother is an independent entity who can decide to be absent or present at will."

The neurophysiological processes in the infant, which prior to the developmental thrust had achieved a patterned integration of the experience "mother" as the result of interaction with this aspect of his environment on one level, had now to be reorganized on a higher level to include new, more extensive perceptions which in some respects impinged on and in others deviated from the already laid-down familiar pattern. At such a point of disruption of an established constellation, anxiety makes its appearance.

Were we to interpret Escalona's observation as evidence that separation from the mother is in itself the cause of the anxiety, we would perhaps be describing an immediate precipitating cause in a specific developmental situation in the infancy of a specific organism. In this sense, there are many "causes" of fear. But we would have said nothing about the principle, either in neurological terms, or on higher evolutionary levels in psychological terms, upon which fear and anxiety are based as they appear in all living organisms, nor about their function in relation to the maintenance of life processes in the ever-present struggle against the existence

---

* In a study of curiosity in infants from six months to two years W. Menaker[9] observed the operation both of the incongruous stimulus and of transitional developmental stages in producing anxiety. With the maturation of ego, anxiety was reduced, curiosity took over, and the stimulus was mastered.

of disruptive factors in the environment. Thus, fear or anxiety belong to the life process as it is manifested in the constant, reciprocal interaction of organism and environment.
They are mediated by hierarchical levels of nervous organization which depend on the evolutionary level of the organism. It is the manifestations of fear which evolve, as these
parallel the neurophysiological organization. These manifestations will differ in content from species to species, and
in degree from individual to individual within a species, as
well as according to developmental levels. In all cases, however, they will represent a species-characteristic way of
perceiving and responding to environmental stimuli which
threaten the patterned, integrated functioning of the organism, and therefore its survival.

Let us turn from these general evolutionary concerns
regarding the meaning of fear and anxiety to their specific
meaning in relation to man. We have attempted to show that
the emergence of consciousness, the development of in-
ordinately intricate differentiations in the central nervous
system of man, called for the evolution of an organizing
process, a co-ordinating psychological entity, which we called
ego. It is through ego that thought processes and behavior
are synthesized, that conflicting impulses are resolved, that
emotions are felt and expressed. The ego process domi-
nates the psychological life of man in that it mediates by
far the greater part of all function in the interaction with
inner and outer environments. If, as has been shown by
the animal studies of Hebb, and those of ethologists like
Lorenz, the reaction and behavior of an animal depends not
merely on the nature of peripheral stimuli, but on the central
state or pattern of the animal's receiving apparatus at the
time of stimulation, how much more is this the case for man
whose functioning depends on an awareness patterned not

only by the memory of past experience, but by the ongoing co-ordinating function of ego as it deals with each new experience.

It becomes apparent, therefore, that in relation to anxiety, which as we have shown above represents a reaction to disruptive forces in the environment, ego, as the organizer of experience, must be the executor of all aspects of the anxiety situation. Ego mediates the perception of the danger or threat from environmental factors by co-ordinating the immediate stimulus with existing neural patterns, thus giving specific meaning to the present in terms of the past and of the total reaction of the organism.* It is through ego that the conscious awareness of this meaning is translated not only into thought and idea, but into the affect, "anxiety." And it is ego, charged as it were through the evolution of its organizing function with the task of ensuring the physical and psychological survival of the organism, which responds to the danger signal by instituting measures of reintegration and resynthesis within the psychic life which will deal with the threat. These measures will naturally vary with the character of the danger and will range from flight or fight reactions to the setting up of repressive and other defensive intrapsychic processes in response to dangers arising from within the organism. Such inner dangers have been described in this connection by Freud[10] as resulting from conflicting or unacceptable impulses, or from excessive quantity of impulse which cannot be assimilated or integrated by the organism. There are also disruptive processes which arise in the interpersonal interactions of human beings and which therefore produce anxiety. Sullivan emphasizes the threatening nature of the disapproval of loved persons in the life of the child. The ego must deal with such anxiety by altering either

---

* When we refer to environment in this context, we mean inner physiological and psychological states, as well as external environment.

the pattern of behavior or the nature of the interpersonal relationship. In either case, a new synthesis is called for.

It would be a mistake to regard the subjective experience of anxiety as exclusively negative and thus to view the ego's attempt to deal with it as purely defensive. Nor is anxiety only positive in the sense that it is a warning that an existing state of integration is being disrupted, survival is being threatened, and appropriate action in the face of danger must be taken. Anxiety may be a spur to new and advanced levels of ego competency. The reorganization and repatterning demanded of ego may go beyond the task of eliminating the danger and reinstating the former stability of the organism to one of creating a higher order of ego function. This may become manifest in physical mastery, intellectual activity, creativity, social interaction, or moral and ethical *niveau*. We see such processes of the positive function of anxiety in the individual, wherein, as the carrier of innovations, he becomes the vehicle of sociocultural evolution. We see them also in social and cultural entities where institutionalized measures for dealing with anxiety may interact with individual ones to stabilize society and ultimately advance it. Thus, there is not only a survival function of anxiety, but an evolutionary one.

In Salteaux Indian society as described by Hallowell,[11] the fear of disease and the interpretation of it by these primitive peoples as resulting from "bad conduct" on the part of the individual or his predecessors acts as a deterrent for "bad," "sinful," or socially unacceptable behavior, thus preserving a certain modicum of societal integration and stability. The socializing function of anxiety as observed in this culture parallels that of the individual in psychoanalytic theory. The fear of punishment for forbidden impulses as described by Freud[12] leads the individual to inhibit such impulses, and to set up within his own personality a critical faculty, known as conscience or "super-ego" whose function it is to deter the expression of anti-social behavior.

Whenever the survival of a species depends on social organization, we know that there will have evolved regulatory patterns which to a greater or lesser extent determine the behavior and interaction of individuals. For example, that pack animals such as wolves obey their leader is such an evolved behavior pattern, and it is more than likely that fear mediates the effectiveness of this pattern. In man, whose survival also depends on social organization, whether the limited family unit or larger social entities, it is ego spurred by anxiety which integrates social requirements and individual needs into a more or less successful adaptive pattern.

We have greatly emphasized earlier in this book that man's evolution takes place in psychosocial rather than genetic terms, and that this is achieved through the reciprocal interaction of social environment and individual ego processes as these influence each other. What is the role of anxiety in this interaction? We have described anxiety as a reaction to disruptive environmental influences. In a societal structure that is evolving, there are in the very nature of change and transition disruptive factors which at one and the same time call forth anxiety and offer opportunities for new levels of ego organization. In the relatively rigid structure of primitive societies in which the causes of and measures for dealing with anxiety are presented, the individual ego has an exceedingly limited opportunity for reintegrating the anxiety situation in its own individual terms. Characteristically, this makes for a stable society, but not for one that exhibits evolutionary advance. The term "primitive" can be understood not only to apply to the simplicity of technological achievement and to the absence of written language, but also to the fixity and inflexibility of social forms and interactions. Like the "overspecialization" of certain anatomical structures in the animal world, they are dead-end roads in the evolutionary process.

Such is not the case for Western civilization, for example. History demonstrates social process in continual change. From ancient to medieval to modern times, change includes every aspect of human life: economic form, religious beliefs, social structure, scientific knowledge, artistic creation, philosophical attitudes, the nature of human interaction, and moral and ethical value systems. These vary from one era to another and from one national group to another. Viewed as an entire panorama of social events moving through time, the changes constitute an evolutionary process which is still going on and of which we are a part. This is not to say that each step within the process necessarily represents an advance. However, as a whole, the increasing complexity and differentiation of all aspects of social structure as they interact with each other and with individuals within the society, creating new environmental niches and new opportunities for ego expansion, justify the application of the term evolution. The very ego which makes use of new niches is the same which itself evolves to increasing complexity of function, and in turn influences the social milieu.

In the midst of this rapidly moving interaction, ego, as the synthesizing agent in man, is under constant pressure to assimilate the advances of sociocultural evolution. In the ontogenetic development of each individual ego, this may become a source of anxiety. Each succeeding generation has the problem of synthesizing the increasingly complex products of cultural evolution. For this, greater ego complexity and autonomy and new ways of dealing with anxiety are required. Take as a simple and relatively superficial example the myriad visual and auditory stimuli resulting from our technological advances which the ego of a modern urban small child is called upon to assimilate and integrate into a usable, patterned whole that will leave him reasonably free of anxiety. There are the incessant raucous sounds of city vehicles: automobiles, buses, fire engines; the sounds of jet planes in the skies; the closer sounds of blaring radios and television sets; the confusion of excited human voices echoing in narrow courtyards; bright lights; the passing of rapidly moving objects; a world surfeited with stimuli. True, the child is not plunged suddenly into this environment, but grows with and into it, so that to some extent his ability to integrate experience keeps pace developmentally with his perceptual apparatus. Nevertheless, his task is not only different from that of a child in a primitive culture, but more complex. He has many more "awarenesses" to synthesize, and thus the sources for anxiety have been multiplied.

In the mastery of the disruptive forces that produce anxiety, ego grows and evolves. This does not mean that anxiety is "good" for human life and should be cultivated. Neither is it "bad," except that its pathological forms lead to unhappiness and malfunction. Anxiety and its counterpart fear are simply the inevitable outcomes of the evolution of life as this process reveals its divergence from the universal law of the increase in entropy. They are hierarchical elaborations of the irritability and reactivity of protoplasm responding to disruptive influences in its biosphere in the service of adaptation and further evolution.

In an expanding, fluid society such as that of the United States, we have an unusual opportunity to observe processes of psychosocial evolution and to see how they impinge upon individual ego development and often create anxiety. Psychoanalysis has taught us that the individual consolidates his sense of identity, i.e., achieves an awareness of who he is, partly through the perception of his own inner states and bodily functions, partly through identification with parents and subsequently other meaningful individuals in the environment, and partly through the definition of his role by the social framework within which he finds himself. In a society created out of diverse human elements, in a physical situation of great expandability founded on a philosophy which extols the creation of new opportunities for growth in all areas, the individual will not find his role rigidly defined by society. Rather, he is likely to experience anxiety because he has conflict in synthesizing that part of his identity which derives from parental figures with that part which comes from his aspiration to take advantage of the opportunities of a new social niche.

Very often in our clinical work, patients come to us with precisely this type of anxiety. A young wife, whom we shall call Jeanne, grew up in a tradition-bound home of immigrant parents in a community in which her family belonged to a minority group. Her parents had rigid ideas about the role of a young woman. She was expected to marry at an early age and raise a family. Higher education or a career of any kind for a young lady were frowned upon. To Jeanne, however, the opportunities of the larger milieu beckoned. She had literary talent and was determined to make a career for herself as a writer. That she might have to repeat her mother's limited life terrified her. It was in some measure this anxiety which, added to the normal impulse toward fuller self-realization, was responsible for the great efforts which she made to get an education and training for her chosen field.

Why did she reject an identification with her mother? The psychoanalytic answer would lie in the area of her interaction with her mother in the course of her development, with special emphasis on the frustrations and rejections which she experienced at her hands, and the resultant ambivalent feelings which she must then have had. The focus is on drives and needs which were not adequately met and on the hostile emotions which followed. An identification based on mixed emotions of love and hate is inevitably incomplete, and identity based upon it is not successfully consolidated. This explanation finds confirmation in many cases, as well as in the very case under discussion. However, it is limited to a narrow frame of reference, and thus, when applied as a total explanation, becomes a half truth. What is omitted is first, the ego striving of both individuals, mother and daughter, which we have described as an aspect of evolution, and second, the evolutionary factors in the sociocultural situation.

Let us be specific. Jeanne's mother grew up within a culture in which her social role was rigidly defined. This included not only the assignment to be exclusively wife and mother, but the demeaning social attitudes toward woman as an inferior being. While there was the possibility within this framework for the gratification of maternal and wifely impulses, the social niche presented no opportunity for the fulfillment or expression of other needs, much less ego expansion. On the contrary, the very assignment of the role carried with it the implication of disparagement in regard to the expression of any individual needs. Frustration of ego evolutionary impulses must certainly be the lot of an individual born into such a social structure.

Jeanne's mother then experienced a transplantation into a sociocultural milieu which presented considerable opportunity for expansion of experience and expressiveness, namely the present-day open-ended society of the United States. In her case, she rejected this opportunity; one might guess that it was because her identity was already securely and rigidly organized around her previously defined role. Environmental opportunity was experienced too exclusively as a disruptive force to an already synthesized structure; availing herself of it would have produced too much anxiety. Aside from any personality maladjustment or neurosis arising from purely intrapsychic conflicts (there were many in this instance),

Jeanne's mother, measured purely in terms of her *interaction* with her larger social environment, was destined to be unfulfilled, unhappy, frustrated, and anxious.* All of these emotions were communicated to Jeanne in the mother's interaction with her child.

It is inevitable then that for Jeanne in the course of growing up the process of identification with her mother should have been split up into several incompatible parts. There is first the unconscious, automatic identification in early childhood with the loving, nurturing part of her mother which goes hand in hand with the child's love for her. There is also some unconscious identification with the mother's unhappiness, frustration, and anxiety. But the growing ego of the child often clamors for the opportunity to fulfill itself optimally, to actualize in real function all its potentialities, to move beyond its origins to new levels of competency and efficacy. And when the sociocultural environment presents this opportunity, the child will make use of it and will identify with the values which are inherent in the opportunity. Thus, there will be conflict between identifications based on the familial experience and those deriving from the environmental opportunity. In this disruptive situation which impedes the ego's function of consolidating an identity, the danger is more likely to be felt as coming from the retrogressive forces, i.e., in a case such as Jeanne's, from the early identifications with the mother; such forces, to the extent that they are conscious, are experienced with anxiety and are rejected.

It might be said that the anxiety which Jeanne experienced consciously, that she might become like her mother, served

---

* It is important that the emphasis here be on *interaction*, for we do not wish to imply that any particular social environment can solve man's problems of adaptation; although certain environments are more favorable to psychosocial evolution than others.

the purposes of her own maturation as well as of psychological evolution. However, for the human being, anxiety is a many-faceted emotion, and for Jeanne the experience of turning away from the model of her mother to a new kind of ego organization was in itself attended with anxiety and with an exclusively human feeling with which we shall concern ourselves presently: *guilt*. But first a few words about Jeanne's anxiety specifically stemming from her choice of her own individual pathway for the expansion and fulfillment of her ego strivings. She came into treatment for help with this anxiety, as well as for an accompanying tendency toward depression. Expressed subjectively, it took the form of: "Will I make it? Will I be adequate to the task I have set myself? Will I succeed?" Translated into terms in which we have defined anxiety, these become questions of psychological survival in the face of pressure on ego processes to synthesize elements that might become disruptive: the conflicting identifications already mentioned, the actual task of testing out abilities in new areas of function, the carrying out of individual goals in the face of familial disapproval, and within a social framework which presents all the complexities of interpersonal interactions and competitive attitudes. That some of Jeanne's anxiety was neurotic in terms of its excessive manifestations and its source in unconscious, unacceptable impulses is undoubtedly true; but much of it was real and the inevitable outcome of her participation in a psychosocial, evolutionary process. The half-conscious awareness of her neuroticism unfortunately only augmented the real anxiety concerning her survival competency. In the therapeutic undertaking, it would not only be a mistake to fail in making a distinction between the two types of anxiety, but it would also be insufficient to deal solely with the so-called neurotic anxiety. How one can help a patient with anxiety stemming unavoidably from the psychoevolutionary process will be treated in Chapter XIII.

To return to Jeanne: the fact is she did "make it." She received an excellent education. She held a position as a writer, with opportunities for some creative expression of her own; she made a good marriage by her own free choice to a man for whom she felt genuine love and affection. One might also add that in terms of our conception of the "new patient" her searching out and making use of the opportunity for psychotherapy represented the successful expansion of her ego. In all areas of ego function her life manifests a distinct advance over her mother's. That the task of synthesizing these advances was experienced with anxiety we have already accounted for. But in the course of Jeanne's treatment, there were many situations which gave rise to clear expressions of guilt in relation to her mother. Apologetic for her own freedom, happiness, and enjoyment, she felt constrained to spend more than the usual amount of time with her mother.

This is certainly not the guilt of conscious sinfulness or wrongdoing. Psychoanalysts might protest that the rebelliousness and oppositionalism involved in her breaking away from the prescribed mores of her group as represented by her family were manifestations of aggressive drives and wishes and that it was for these that Jeanne felt guilty. We would not deny the existence in our patient of such feelings and wishes, some of them conscious, others unconscious. How could it be otherwise? This frustrated and unhappy mother could scarcely have met all the little girl's needs for mothering. Yet, the bringing to light of these and other intrafamilial sources of guilt had little effect on her feelings. She was overwhelmed by unhappiness for her mother's plight, unable to enjoy her own good fortune fully, and inspired with the need to assume responsibility for doing something to help her mother. Her strong empathic tendency was not confined to her mother. She was a person capable of more than the usual amount of sympathy and understanding for the difficulties of others, and often put her feelings into helpful action. To view these reactions exclusively as compensations or reaction-formations against opposing hostile and sadistic impulses would be to disregard and fail to explore fully an important source of their psychobiological origin: the very same source in fact which is responsible for the instituting of compensations.

In Chapter IX, we have described in the interaction between mother and child the development of the ability to identify with and to empathize with another human being. This begins in the mother's reactions to the infant in the feeding situation, wherein her sensitivity to his reactions, as well as his active co-operation, as Escalona has said, "constitutes the earliest mutual (instead of one-sided) adaptation between mother and infant."[8] In this interaction, the cornerstone is laid for that aspect of loving which consists in understanding and meeting the needs of another. As the infant grows and develops, he perceives this capacity in his mother and incorporates it as part of his own equipment. The exact nature of such incorporation, whether imitation or identification, will change as he matures, but at each level of development will take a form appropriate to it. These identifications are mediated by ego processes to begin with, and, in turn, become part of ego. The capacity to identify with another individual because the building of ego depends on it is as essential to human survival as the ability to fly is for the nestling.* Thus human beings, living through a long

---

* Freud saw the importance of the identification process in relation to super-ego formation, as this was vital for the socialization of man. He derived it, however, from the instinctual impulse conflicts implicit in the

pedamorphic period, are endowed with and have acquired in varying degrees the ability to identify with and empathize with another. This is an important and essential aspect of loving; conversely, the original loving situation of mother and child is essential to the development of this capacity.

How are these facts related to the problem of guilt? Since man lives and survives only in a social situation, albeit the original family unit or the larger social milieu, he is witness from very early in his life to differences in the endowment and opportunity of individuals. The social scene is inevitably, for human awareness, a comparative one. There are the strong and the weak, the intelligent and the stupid, the powerful and the submissive, the healthy and the diseased, the young and the old, the happy and the unhappy, the fulfilled and the unfulfilled, the fortunate and the unfortunate. In large measure, these are the consequence of the operation of randomness in evolution: the randomness of a particular individual's constitution, both physical and psychic, of his particular place in historical, socio-evolutionary time, of his social and economic opportunities—in other words, the accident of the niche into which he was born. Certainly, within limits man can and does do something about changing this niche, both in his individual life and on the larger social scene. In fact, his very individual existence changes the niche for those other individuals whose lives impinge upon and interact with his. This is the evolutionary process as we have attempted to describe it.

Yet, much of what man must experience is a consequence of a randomness over which he has no control. When it operates to the disadvantage of someone with whom he is iden-

---

Oedipal situation, not from primary ego capacities as they exist "embryonically" from the beginning of life, unfold, and are formed by the continual interaction of organism and environment.

tified, and to his own advantage, he experiences guilt. He wishes for the other individual with whom he empathizes something of the same advantage and opportunity which he himself experiences. This is so because the identification is based on an initial situation in which the mother's understanding for her child included her wish within the limits of her capacity to provide him with optimal opportunities for growth and fulfillment. Thus, the very capacity for identification which is essential to man's survival leads him inevitably to a feeling of guilt, as he perceives the randomness of nature, whether he calls it the injustice of fate or builds it into an ethical system of rewards and punishments.

So fundamental and so painful is this aspect of the experience of guilt which arises from the interaction of awareness, identification, and the chance circumstances of evolution that man has sought innumerable ways of lessening its impact. One of them has been to suppress feelings of empathy or at least strongly to delimit the emotional involvement with others, so that guilt feelings will not be called into play. The manner in which this takes place varies from culture to culture, from one historical period to another, and from individual to individual within a society.

If man can account for guilt in terms of his own sinfulness or misdeeds, there is a chance of expiation. The conception of illness as punishment for some wrongdoing in the thinking of the Salteaux described above is such an example. Such a view diminishes the identification with the unfortunate individual because his fellows know that if he confesses his sin he will regain health, thereby shifting the cause of the misfortune (the disease, in this case) from natural events inherent in the life processes to the individual's own responsibility, and providing a solution for his dilemma. Conversely, because of guilt for a privileged social position, arising in the wake of identification processes with other less privileged individuals, and in an effort to keep out of awareness both the identification and the guilt, man has sought to explain his good fortune as the result of some special virtue which entitles him to it.

Since Jeanne neither repressed the guilt nor its accompanying identification, but experienced it vis-à-vis her mother, we might attribute to her a certain tolerance for the naturalness of a guilt that arose out of her perception of her more favored environmental niche. Such guilt could only be called neurotic if it actually were to impede her functioning seriously, or if it prevented her from pursuing her own independent life goals. Although there were neurotic tendencies in this direction, they were never victorious over her very vital, expansive ego strivings.

That much of man's suffering is inextricably linked to what we would like to call the ego evolutionary aspect of the problem of guilt has been the theme of mythology, the Bible, and great literature, as well as the concern of philosophers, e.g., Kierkegaard. The story of Cain and Abel, a theme which Steinbeck has taken as the *leitmotif* for *East of Eden*, is illustrative of our interpretation of guilt arising out of the conflict between survival need and identification operating in an environment in which arbitrariness prevails. Cain experiences rejection at the hands of God (the Father) because his sacrifice is not acceptable, whereas his brother's sacrifice is affirmed and received. In a rage at this injustice, which corresponds in the individual to the randomness of nature in evolutionary change, he murders his brother, Abel. It is not so apparent, in the face of the injustice, that he is indeed guilty of the murder in moral terms. Rather, is it not that Cain assumes the feeling of guilt—takes the guilt upon himself—because to do otherwise would be to question the justice of God's act? This he dare not do; rather, he must deny the injustice and preserve a righteous conception of

God. Why cannot Cain face the injustice of God's act? To do so would be to destroy the good image of God, to commit psychological murder of the idealized father, and this he cannot do. He needs to preserve this image as a basis for that identification with the good father on which his own ego formation and therefore his survival depend.

Ego formation and the experience of being loved and loving are inevitably bound together, since identification with the first loved one, the mother, is essential to the beginning of important integrative aspects of ego formation. It follows obviously that experiences of rejection* are antithetical to ego development, but except for extreme cases which may result in psychosis or severe neurosis, the momentum of developmental ego processes seems to tend automatically toward a mastery of the rejection. To some extent, and within limits, this takes place through the direct or indirect expression of hostility. But very importantly, the ego masters either the explicit rejection of a specific situation or the rejections imposed by the vicissitudes of life's randomness, by an act of primitive causal thinking, i.e., of apportioning blame to itself, and experiencing a feeling of guilt. Guilt of this sort exists not primarily *because* of hostility or hostile acts but because of the need to deny reality and maintain the good image of the loved-one,[13] whether mother, father, or God—and this, in the service of psychological survival. It is notable that Steinbeck writes that we are all children of Cain, not of Abel. This does not only mean that we all experience guilt, but also that it is Cain who survives, albeit at the cost of the suffering associated with guilt feeling.

It would seem then that just as fear and anxiety are the

---

* Rejection is hereby meant to emphasize those experiences that are hurtful to ego processes: to the self-image, to self-esteem, and to the perception of reality for example, and not exclusively to the failure to gratify drive needs in the Freudian sense.

inevitable concomitants of the life process as it struggles against disruptive environmental influences, so guilt is an inevitable accompaniment of ego formation as it serves the function of survival. We might hypothesize that as ego evolves to higher levels of organization, which would include not only the mastery of physical reality but the understanding of the very facts about man and his psychobiological position in the evolving stream of life which we have attempted to formulate, it will be able to tolerate anxiety more successfully and synthesize identifications on the basis of more realistic perceptions of others, thereby experiencing less guilt.

Certainly, in our disquisition on anxiety and guilt, we have omitted many aspects of these phenomena. This is not intended as an exhaustive coverage of the manifestations, causes, and consequences of various forms of anxiety and guilt as they appear in the normal and the neurotic individual. Our purpose is to select only that which we feel is relevant to the question of man's psychological evolution, especially as it pertains to ego, and to show how this evolution is continuous with evolving streams of life and obeys its general laws, although having specific characteristics of its own.

• REFERENCES

1. Freedman, L. Z., and Roe, A.: Evolution and human behavior. In Roe, A., and Simpson, G. G., Eds.: *Behavior and Evolution.* Yale University Press, New Haven, 1958, p. 461.
2. Darwin, C.: *The Descent of Man.* Random House, New York, 1936, p. 448.
3. May, R.: *The Meaning of Anxiety.* Ronald Press, New York, 1950.

4. Goldstein, K.: *The Organism.* American Book, New York, 1939.
5. Freud, S.: *The Problem of Anxiety.* W. W. Norton, New York, 1936.
6. Robinson, V. P.: *Jessie Taft: A Professional Biography.* University of Pennsylvania Press, Philadelphia, 1962, p. 179.
7. Hebb, D. O.: On the nature of fear. *Psychoanalytic Review* 53: 259-276, 1953.
8. Escalona, Sibylle: Emotional Development in the First Year of Life, *Problems of Infancy and Childhood.* Transactions of the 6th Conference, March 17-18. Josiah Macy, Jr., Foundation, New York, 1952.
9. Menaker, W.: Neugier im 1. und 2. Lebensjahr. *Zeitschrift für Psychologie,* Bd. 137, 1936, pp. 131-167.
10. Freud, S.: *The Problem of Anxiety.* W. W. Norton, New York, 1936.
11. Hallowell, A. I.: The social function of anxiety in a primitive society. *American Sociological Review* 6: 869-881, 1941.
12. Freud, S.: The passing of the Oedipus complex. *Collected Papers,* Vol. II. Hogarth Press, London, 1953, pp. 269-276.
13. Menaker, E.: Masochism: a defense reaction of the ego. *Psychoanalytic Quarterly* 22: 205-220, 1953.

11 · THE ROLE OF CONFLICT IN EVOLUTION

CONCEPTS, like living organisms, are the product of a history from which it is difficult to extricate them. Conflict is such a concept. Generally, the term has strong negative implications in our civilization and historical period, although this was by no means true throughout man's history. Whether we refer to a struggle for power, position, and possession among nations, groups, or individuals themselves, to emotional disharmony in the interaction between individuals, or to intrapsychic disturbance and its accompanying subjective experience, conflict is viewed as an unacceptable state of events to be avoided, reduced to a minimum, or, at the very worst, resignedly tolerated as an inevitable part of life. However, during the period concurrent with and following the great discoveries concerning evolution, conflict was extolled as the prime mover in man's progress. Taking Darwin's principle of natural selection and the "survival of the fittest" as a model for social theory, thinkers like Herbert Spencer made a virtue of conflict as the driving force responsible for pushing man toward the final goal of his social evolution as they saw it, a perfect society.

Before we comment on this misapplication of evolutionary principles, it might be well to point out how difficult it is for man to observe phenomena, and especially those which impinge on his emotions, without placing them within the framework of a value system. This fact has its logic anchored in the evolutionary process itself, since man's survival depends on his becoming a socially functioning creature to which the internalization of values is essential. Furthermore, man's conscious awareness, which includes his knowledge of evolution and his place in its hierarchy as a dominant species, to the extent that it affirms life, must place a positive value on evolution. It is not difficult to see, then, how the nineteenth-century social philosophers, in their enthusiasm for evolutionary theory, took social conflict to be a literal reflection or continuation of a biological process, and called it and its social products, "good."

Since the concept of "fitness" in human affairs is never simply definable as the capacity for physical survival through the reproductive period, but includes social, intellectual, creative, and moral "fitness," all of which are relative to a given social structure at a given historical period, and all of which interact with one another and thus contribute through a multiplicity of unpredictable combinations to social advance, the interpretation of human history in terms of what is momentarily dominant as necessarily "good" can only lead to fallacy and misuse. Dobzhansky[1] expresses this in the following statement:

> One thing which is clear is that the fittest is not necessarily a romantic figure, or a victorious conqueror, or a superman. He is most likely to be merely a prolific parent. Social Darwinists did not know, or did not want to know any of these subtleties and qualifications. They equated affluence and occupation of the seats of the mighty with biological fitness, and economic laissez-faire, cut-throat competition, and rivalry with natural selection.

Thus, the concept of conflict became the justification in pseudo-biological terms for upholding a specific social order, for doctrines of racial, class, or national superiority, and fell legitimately into ill repute.

In regard to conflict, the thinking of the social evolutionists was further contaminated by the principle of "finalism." Herbert Spencer viewed the struggle for existence as tending toward the perfectibility of man and his society. This placed the concept of conflict in a scientifically untenable teleological position. Evolution, biological, cultural, and psychological, can only be defined in terms of its existence and direction. To attribute ultimate purpose to it in terms of a finite goal is anthropomorphic thinking.

The concept of conflict emerged again in a central position in psychoanalytic thought, in which its relationship to evolution is not immediately obvious, but nevertheless present. Freud saw the individual ego emerging out of the undifferentiated id, the unconscious repository of instinctual impulses, primarily as a result of conflict. From early infancy on, the instinctual frustrations and deprivations which the child experiences lead to the awareness of differentiation between self and non-self.[2] Thus, the conflict between drive need and the limited extent of fulfillment creates the pressure out of which ego is structured.

It is true that this point of view has been modified by the work of Hartmann, *et al.*, who have posited a "conflict-free" ego sphere, indigenously present. This is nevertheless a limited concept. It has been *added to* the theory of ego emergence under the pressure of conflict; it does not replace it. Nor does it view ego as a primary psychological process precipitated out of the evolution of the nervous system and continuing to evolve in the interaction with the changing social and cultural environment.

According to Freud, conflict plays another important role in the development of personality, namely in its socialization. Again, the frustration of an instinctual need, this time a sexual need in early childhood, i.e., the Oedipal wishes, is responsible for an identification with the parent who forbids the fulfillment of the wish. The psychic incorporation of the forbidding parent becomes the basis for conscience, or as Freud called it, the super-ego. The ability to comply with social demands stems from the resolution of the Oedipus conflict and the resultant formation of the super-ego.[3] Thus, in ontogenetic terms, Freud viewed both the development of ego and super-ego as outgrowths of conflict. The theme of the opposition between instinctual drive needs and the demands of society characterizes his conception of the etiology of the neuroses, and his view of the inevitably tragic plight of man as expressed in *Civilization and Its Discontents*.[4] For he saw the conflict between instinct and civilization as unresolvable in any productive way and foresaw the possibility that man might destroy himself on the basis of the untameability of the aggressive instinct.

Such a view, in our opinion, has several sources of error. One is the application of limited ontogenetic observations to a phylogenetic process. Furthermore, conflict is not exclusively responsible either for the formation of ego and super-ego structures or for the relationship of man to the problems of social adaptation. We have tried to emphasize that consciousness and ego represent the *positive* gains of an evolutionary process, acquired by man through interaction with environment and to show how these acquisitions participate in furthering social evolution, and through interaction with social change, themselves change. In such a view, the concept of conflict for human evolution gives way essentially to one of interaction within an ongoing dynamic process. The danger of interpreting man's social behavior either as the legitimate continuation of nature's ruthless struggle for survival* or of hopelessly irreconcilable forces is reduced to a minimum.

In an earlier chapter, we were concerned with the driving force and directional nature of evolution in its hierarchical advance to more complex forms. It would perhaps be more accurate to speak in this connection of a disequilibrium of forces. The directional nature of a process is inevitably determined by a disequilibrium of forces: the process being influenced *in its direction* by the greater force. In the emergence of life from the infinite variety and complexity of interactions in the world of inorganic compounds, it was the "inability to reach equilibrium"[5] which was crucial to this event. It was thus that the second law of thermodynamics was breached, that the principle of entropy was negated within the system "life." But life, having begun, had to maintain itself in a continuing struggle against the disrupting forces in the environment. To do this, it had to evolve. *Evolution is life's answer to the principle of entropy.* If we divest the concept of conflict from all its human value

---

* Even here, as Dobzhansky[1] points out, ". . . struggle is not necessarily contention, warfare or bloodshed. Animals and plants 'struggle' to avoid the perils of cold, heat, desiccation, drowning, gale winds, etc., but they do not freeze, burn, or drown other individuals of their own or of other species."

judgment implications and apply it to the disequilibrium of forces which is ever present in the interaction of organism and environment, then in this sense, and in this sense alone, is it the driving force of evolution.

We must be careful not to equate evolution with change alone. For within the hierarchical advance of organisms there exists stability, e.g., in the form of species and individuals. This stability is maintained at certain threshold levels which, when exceeded by disruptive environmental influences, bring about evolutionary change. Von Bertalanffy[6] describes this process with great lucidity: ". . . the living organism can be defined by stating that it is not a closed system with respect to its surroundings, but an open system which continually gives up matter to the outer world and takes in matter from it, but maintains itself in this continuous exchange, in a steady state, or approaches such steady state in its variations in time. . . . The organism as a whole is, however, never in true equilibrium. . . . The steady state which the system approaches is defined by the approach of minimal entropy production. From this arises the revolutionary consequence that in the transition to a steady state within an open system there may be a decrease in entropy and a spontaneous transition to a state of higher heterogeneity and complexity."

We have defined conflict for organic evolution in terms of a disequilibrium of forces operating within the system "organism-environment." How does such a seemingly remote evolutionary conception of conflict affect our understanding of man and his psychological and sociocultural evolution? Long before the advent of man, the genetic evolution of the neurophysiological substratum for behavior created the bridge between organic and psychosocial evolution. The ethologists have demonstrated the existence of discrete, innate behavior patterns in organisms which must have evolved under selection pressure to be as species-specific as morphological structures. Such behavior patterns can only reflect a corresponding neurophysiological patterning, even if the parallel does not exist in a one-to-one relationship.[7] Here, the imbalance of the forces of the environment as against those within the organism (conflict in the broadest sense) which leads, by processes of evolution, to the selection of certain optimally adaptive behavior patterns plays itself out in an added dimension: the individual organism in the specific environmental situation, which, because of the variations that it presents may create conflict between the general behavior pattern and its concrete, detailed application. For example, the nest-building behavior of the robin is laid down in its general pattern: There is a specific size of nest, there are specific materials for its construction, there are special kinds of location for its placement, there are specific movements associated with its construction. Yet, each of these specifications has a range of modifiability according to the situation of the robin and the environment. It is conceivable that sometimes the environment may offer a wide range of nest-building materials, that at other times it might be much more limited, and that perhaps substitutions might need to be instituted.

There are also situations in which environmental stimuli may simultaneously release opposing behavior patterns, e.g., eating and caring for the young, thereby creating conflict. Whether the environment affords opportunity or exerts pressure would be critical, in the behavioral sphere, for the creation of that type of conflict—a forced choice within a given range of behavioral possibility—which leads to modifiability. At higher levels in the animal scale, we might refer in this connection to learning. Thus, the increasing plasticity of nervous-system reactions as we ascend the evolutionary ladder is testimony to the resolution of the basic evolutionary conflict in favor of life's increasing adaptability. Yet, this very plasticity, through the expansions of the biosphere that it makes possible, creates demands for new adaptations. Stated differently, we might say that a decrease in specialization, inasmuch as it represents some loss of stability, based on an enormous increase in the complexity of nervous-system organization, particularly as it applies in the behavioral sphere, creates conflict of a new order.

This new order of conflict finds its ultimate expression in man. We do not refer here to neurotic conflict, nor yet to subjective conflict. That is a particular aspect of a larger problem, with which we will deal presently. By conflict in man, in this sense, we mean his characteristic relationship to environment which entails the participation of consciousness and ego integrative processes in the countless details of his life, upon which disruptive environmental influences may impinge, namely the physical, emotional, intellectual, and social. This is not necessarily conflict in the sense of strife, contention, or unhappiness, but rather life's ever-present demand for balance which involves man in an active series of conscious choices, plans, thoughts, feelings, and an infinite variety of their combinations which may lead to action. Such is the consequence of his neural evolution that the more simplified, automatic interaction with the environment of lower forms has in large measure ceded to conscious control. He must forge the environment and himself into a relatively stable whole.

However, it is important to note that the complexity of man's psychic life, the extensiveness of his mental apparatus, and the variety of situations with which he must deal necessitate that he retain the ability for automatic response in the case of elemental functions. This is one aspect of unconscious psychic phenomena. Nevertheless, through the symbolic representations which are the content of consciousness, man is not only removed from an immediate contact with reality as we have stated earlier, but he must assume responsibility for mediating between his own organism and environment either in terms of achieving some homeostatic balance or of resynthesizing the elements and events of a disruptive situation on a new and higher level. It is ego which performs this function, and to the extent that it meets the challenge of disorganizing forces, it can be said to be dealing with conflict in the broadest sense. This may be in the area of solving a problem, making a discovery, performing a physical feat, controlling or expressing an emotion, caring for another individual, or any of the other countless situations in which an individual ego has the task and the opportunity of functioning.

Such a viewpoint assumes the same active, organizing principle within ego itself which characterizes the life processes as a whole and which has its basis in an equivalent neurophysiological substratum. "All modern electrophysiology indicates that the activity of the brain is continuous and that the effect of a sensory event is not to arouse inactive tissue, but to modify the activity already going on."[8] Ego functions as the executive of those neurological processes. In its contact with environment, it constantly deals with objective conflict, and in so doing changes both the environment and itself. Angyal,[9] speaking not specifically of ego but of the organism's interaction with environment, notes its trend in the direction of an increase in autonomy and describes its activity as having "the aim . . . to master, theoretically or practically, blind heteronomous happenings, to place them at the service of life and to eliminate disturbing influences." Furthermore, in a footnote, he makes an imaginative and seminal comment: "It is very suggestive to assume that the tendency toward increased autonomy is not only the general dynamic trend of the individual organism, but also the 'primum movens' of the phylogenetic process." The tendency toward autonomy is itself set in motion by what Oparin, in speaking of life at the cellular level, calls the "antagonism of the environment," and what we have called conflict in the objective sense. Thus, ego deals with conflict as it copes with the physical and social environment, and conflict in turn mobilizes evolutionary advances in the nature and function of ego.

Since man's sociocultural and psychological evolution is mediated by ego changes, it would be meaningful to discuss a specific ego function which is of the utmost importance in bringing about advance. This is the function of ego-ideal formation. The individual ego has the capacity to synthesize out of the social environment a value system which becomes an individual or group ideal and which then serves to motivate ego function toward thought and behavior in the direction of its realization. Such ego-ideal formation begins in the familial setting as imitation of specific parental traits and attitudes or as a reaction against them. These imitations or their opposites are then consolidated into identifications with the parental figures and constitute a significant portion of the individual's identity. That the love and care of parents, especially of the mother in the earliest levels of development, is the psychological nutriment which is essential for these identification processes and the idealizations that lead to ego-ideal formation has been described in a previous chapter. It is ego itself which has the capacity to synthesize, through a selective perception of reality and a recombination of its elements, a new image in the form of an ideal to be followed. Often, the parental images form only the skeletal structure of such an ego-ideal, and the body of this structure is organized out of other social encounters and contact with culture.

What is important for man's evolution is the capacity of ego to respond to the need to effect a psychic equilibrium in the interaction with social environment by constructing highly individuated images which are not mere duplications of personality characteristics of predecessors, but are new syntheses which become operational models for individual and group conduct. It is not difficult to see that advances in such projected goals may become focal points for social evolution. A society which is sufficiently open-ended and fluid to permit optimal interaction between its members will afford maximal opportunity for the synthesis of new ego-ideal formations among its individual members, thus creating a vast reservoir out of which exceptional individuals will arise who can formulate and express in their creative efforts the striving of a people. These formulated expressions of the ego-ideal, whether heroic acts, scientific discoveries, literary achievements or technological, social and aesthetic advance for example, then become the models for the creation of new ego-ideal formations in the population at large.

Man not only knows about evolution, including his own, in an intellectual, theoretical sense, he experiences it subjectively in that he perceives change in his environment and within himself and is aware, if only dimly, that conflicting emotions are set in motion by the need to reorganize his psychic processes to accommodate such change. In some sense then, man's daily life calls upon him to resolve conflictful situations and to be aware of so doing. The more rapid the changes in his environment, e.g., in periods of social upheaval, the more his ego will be called upon to resynthesize patterns of adaptation and to produce ego change in the process. Such transitions, which are attempts on the behavioral and emotional level to deal with disequilibrium created by environmental factors, will, as we have said above, produce anxiety. Such anxiety is a precipitate of a specific aspect of the evolutionary process in psychological terms; it is not only the result of conflict between instinctual impulses (needs, wishes, drives) and the deprivations, restrictions, and limitations placed on their fulfillment by culture and the need for social adaptation—an aspect of conflict and anxiety emphasized in psychoanalytic theory—but an expression of opposing forces within ego itself.

On the other hand, there are tendencies toward stabilization expressed in social terms through adherence to tradition and in individual terms through a fixity of character structure and behavioral pattern. This tendency of ego to maintain an existing, already achieved pattern of psychic organization can be compared to the biological conservatism of organisms in maintaining their integrity and independence of environmental influences. On the other hand, ego, propelled in part by the conflictual encounter with environment and in part by its inherent capacity as the executor of the life process in man to go beyond its status quo and achieve a maximum of individuation and an optimum of organizational autonomy, will express the advancing, progressive aspect of evolution.

These opposing tendencies constitute an important aspect of ego's relationship to conflict. In the life history of individuals, the quantitative relationship of these opposing tendencies will differ from individual to individual and within the same individual at various points in development and in varying environmental situations. However, in terms of man's total evolution as a species, it is our opinion that the outcome of the conflict between these opposing tendencies points in the direction of advance. This advance is manifest in higher, more complex levels of ego integration, as they have evolved throughout man's history in the interaction between social processes and his psychobiological being.

We cannot leave a discussion of subjective conflict in man without dealing with the question of neurotic conflict in Freud's sense of the term. It is undoubtedly true that the disruptive forces of the external or internal environment can be of such intensity that the ego is called upon to institute defensive measures of such proportions as to interfere with its further normal functioning. The classic example of this is, of course, the creation of hysterical conversion symptoms as a result of the massive repression of sexual impulses. Such impulses are experienced by the individual as forbidden because they are directed toward persons who are tabooed by culture, e.g., incestuous love objects or their surrogates. To repress them, i.e., to ban them from awareness and relegate them to the unconscious, is the ego's way of resolving the conflict between the demand of the impulse for fulfillment and the restraining commands of society. In so doing, however, it gives up, in the creation of the neurotic symptom as the by-product of repression, a large piece of its own freedom of function. Not all neurotic conflicts result in the formation of symptoms; sometimes, the ego's attempts at resolution result in diffuse characterological changes and the impairment to ego function is not so obvious. In fact, there are certain solutions to neurotic conflict which may enhance specific ego functions, perhaps at the expense of others, but nevertheless in such a way as to be productive of positive evolutionary change.*

The ability of ego to institute defenses, i.e., to deal with intrapsychic conflict either by changing the perception of reality or altering the normal responses to it through, e.g., repression, denial, isolation, or reaction formation, is a significant psychological acquisition of evolution.[10] But it is important to remember that the reorganization of reality in terms of defense is only one aspect of the integrative function of ego—an aspect that has been heavily emphasized in psychoanalysis. Because of its origins in a therapeutic concern with the neuroses, psychoanalysis developed a limited defini-

---

* We do not regard all the productive by-products of neurosis as sublimations in the sense that they are derivatives of the sexual instincts. Nor is aesthetic creativity necessarily the by-product of neurotic conflict.

tion of conflict, as existing between opposing tendencies within the three structural components of personality which it posited: id, ego, and super-ego. The function of therapy was then the resolution of conflict through the making conscious of impulses and defenses against them which had been excluded from the area of awareness.

There is perhaps no better proof that the dimensions of conflict are much broader than this than the empirical experience throughout the history of psychoanalysis that the making conscious of conflict between impulse and ego did not invariably or completely resolve the conflict. In the light of an evolutionary hypothesis, the development of ego to a maximum level of individuation is interfered with by the need to sacrifice important aspects of ego function in order to uphold defenses.

For example, in the case of Ralph, a highly over-intellectualized, obsessive patient, it was not enough, in terms of therapeutic help, to make conscious to him his repressed antagonistic feelings toward his father which played a large role in the formation of his neurotic character structure; nor even to help him to relive some of the emotion connected with such feelings. What was crucial for the freeing of his ego was bringing into conscious awareness the extent of his inhibition in the perception of reality, and more specifically, reality in the perception of his father's personality and relationship to him. As it happened, his father, too, had had envious and hostile feelings toward the patient, which the patient had failed to perceive in order to uphold his particular defensive system which involved self-denigration in the name of maintaining certain idealized illusions about his father.

Thus, while the attempted resolution of an intrapsychic conflict through fairly rigid defenses succeeds in establishing a certain homeostatic balance within the personality, it inhibits the free interaction between ego and environment and therefore the resolution of that larger evolutionary conflict which is the challenge of life itself, and through which ego advances to higher levels of organization and individuation. The neurotic conflict can be said to be contra-evolutionary to the extent that the nature and extent of the defenses, which it sets in motion, limit the ego's ability to fulfill its potentialities and seek out its optimal environmental niche. Nevertheless, since there are few if any absolutes in the sphere of human behavior, the particular solution of a neurotic conflict for a given individual may indeed restrict his ego development, and yet be of such a nature that sufficient ego function remains intact for him to make a valuable social contribution. The ontogenetic evolutionary level of an individual ego is by no means a direct function of the nature of his neurotic conflict and obviously does not correspond to the level of sociocultural evolution which his society has reached. It may fall below or exceed it.

Although man's scientific and technological advances repre-sent an increasing mastery of the physical environment, they have so altered the social environment as to create pressure for new adaptations. The tremendous increase in world population, the proximity of peoples, industrialization with resultant urbanization, new social structures, the transition from old to new value systems, scientific and medical discoveries which have conquered many diseases and extended the life span, as well as the invention of implements of war capable of total annihilation of the human species—all these have produced a disequilibrium between social forces in the environment and the individual, calling for ego organization on new and unprecedented levels.

Such ego advances on a psychological level can have meaning for man's sociocultural evolution only if they are socially implemented. This can take place only through communication. Thus, in speaking of social evolution, Ginsberg[11] says: "Mental evolution in man differs radically from mental evolution in the animal world in the part played by social factors, i.e. interaction between minds. This interaction vastly extends the powers of mind, not only directly but indirectly, by enabling its products or achievements to contribute toward further achievements." Through social interaction, the gains in ego evolution are transmitted and influence the advance of society as a whole, whether in the area of morals, ethics, religious belief, philosophy of life, or in what is perhaps society's most important advance, the creation of social institutions which will provide maximum opportunity for the ego expansion, individuation, and expressiveness of its individual members. For sociocultural evolution to take this course, individuals must have the opportunity to cultivate, foster, and extend those basic processes of human interaction on which the very beginnings of ego, from the psychological standpoint, are founded—processes of identification and empathic relatedness to others. We have described these beginnings in the earliest phases of the mother-child relationship, in the course of which the mother's love for her child is crucial to ego formation from its neurophysiological substratum to its complex synthesis out of identification, first with the mother and then with other significant individuals in the child's life. Love and ego development and evolution are not bound together by an arbitrary adherence to a high-sounding altruistic philosophy of life, but by psychobiological necessity and history. A society, therefore, which encourages identification with others, thereby facilitating interaction and communication, fosters the elaboration of higher levels of ego functioning. One which fosters disidentification through the setting up of rigid class lines or through the creation of unaccepted minority groups, for example, impedes social interaction, thus limiting the opportunities for ego expansion by way of a wide range of identification possibilities. The coincidence of higher ethical values with the dynamism of psychosocial evolution points to their common origin in man's struggle to deal with the increasing complexities of his environment by evolving a higher order of ego functioning in an ever-widening portion of the population to be subsequently reflected in his social institutions. These, in turn, will influence the rate and direction of ego evolution.

▪ REFERENCES

1. Dobzhansky, T.: *Mankind Evolving*. Yale University Press, New Haven, 1962, p. 11.
2. Freud, S.: *The Ego and The Id*. W. W. Norton, New York, 1961.
3. Freud, S.: The passing of the Oedipus complex. *Collected Papers*, Vol. II. Hogarth Press, London, 1953, pp. 269-276.
4. Freud, S.: *Civilization and Its Discontents*. Doubleday, New York, 1958.
5. Rush, J. H.: *The Dawn of Life*. Signet, New York, 1957.
6. Von Bertalanffy, L.: *Problems of Life*. Harper & Bros. Torchbooks, New York, 1960, pp. 126, 127.
7. Gerard, R.: Becoming—the residue of change. In Tax, S., Ed.: *The Evolution of Man, Evolution After Darwin*, Vol. II. University of Chicago Press, Chicago, 1960.
8. Hebb, D. O.: The role of neurological ideas in psychology. *Journal of Personality 20:* 39-55, Sept. 1951.
9. Angyal, A.: *Foundations for a Science of Personality*. Commonwealth Foundation, New York, 1941.
10. Freud, A.: *The Ego and the Mechanisms of Defense*. The Hogarth Press and the Institute of Psycho-Analysis, London, 1937.
11. Ginsberg, M.: Social evolution. In Banton, M., Ed.: *Darwinism and the Study of Society*. Quadrangle Books, Chicago, 1961.

12 · ETHICS IN EVOLUTION

WHEN CONSCIOUSNESS EVOLVED in the social animal that is man, the niche was created for the evolution of moral conduct and ethical systems. Precisely this confluence of awareness and relatedness to others accounts for the inevitability of the gradual emergence of ethics as an aspect of man's psychology, without which he would not have survived. It is this naturalistic view of ethics which calls upon no metaphysics, no mysticism, and no theological system to account for its existence which we propose to pursue.

The panorama of the evolution of life reveals both an increase in diversification of organisms and an advance in the complexity and efficacy of their organization in relation to the environment. Biologically, as we have discussed else-where, this process took place under selection pressure on the basis of the genetic transmission of specific characteristics favorable to survival. It is a startling fact, however, that evolution on this level has reached its limits. Thus, Huxley[1] describes the condition of organic evolution as follows: ". . . before the mid-Pleiocene period, some five million years ago, all the purely *physiological* and *material* possibilities of life had been exhausted—size, power, speed, sensory and mus-cular efficiency, chemical coordination, temperature-regula-tion and the rest. After nearly two thousand million years, biological evolution on this planet had reached the limit of its advance." But as Huxley makes clear, "evolution was by no means at an end . . . major advance was still possible, for other major potentialities of life had not been realized . . . its possibilities of fuller awareness, its mental or psychological attributes."

This ultimate outcome of organic evolution, the emergence of neural organization of such complexity that awareness and memory made their appearance, resulted in an entirely new mode for the transmission of evolutionary increments, which in themselves had changed from material to psychic entities. In the evolution of innate behavior patterns as de-scribed by the ethologists, we have an example of the genetic transmission of psychic entities. This genetic transmission, however, takes place at an evolutionary level before the advent of consciousness. The new mode included the evolu-tion of structured entities of a psychological nature which, in analogy to genetic structure, would fix and stabilize human experience so that it could be communicated and transmitted. In the individual, this entity was ego; in the social group, it was culture. Thus, we can speak of psychosocial or socio-cultural evolution.

The transmission of the cultural heritage of man in all its

aspects—artifacts, sociofacts, and mentifacts (a term proposed by Bidney[2])—and the possibility of its improvement by other than genetic means, i.e., by oral and written communication, by the actual presence of artifacts, the actual functioning of social institutions, and the emotional bonds of individuals to one another, increased the rate of evolutionary advance immeasurably. This turning point in the ways of evolution is as crucial to the continuance of life, once it had reached the level of man's awareness, as was the change from the asexual reproduction of the protozoa to sexual reproduction in metazoa.

Within the vast residue of man's remembered experience as reflected and transmitted in a variety of cultural products, there exists the area of moral conduct and its organization into ethical systems. Perhaps in no other sphere of psychosocial evolution is the imperative character of man's social nature so clearly revealed. The necessity for social relatedness is given first in the long pedamorphic period of the child which inaugurates a close emotional relationship between mother and child on which the growing individual's physical and psychological survival depends; second, by the need for social co-operation within the human group to make even the most primitive economy workable; third, by man's need to share, exchange, and communicate experience through verbal interaction, which is a reflection of the increasing refinement of awareness and its emotional concomitants.

Social interaction is thus essential for survival, and becomes in turn the vehicle for further evolution. It would follow then that the evolution of psychologically and culturally organized codes for the regulation of social functioning was most crucial to human survival. Certainly, in the area of sociocultural evolution there must exist within the variety of human acquisitions a hierarchy based on their indispensability for survival.

One might dispense with some artifacts and still survive, but not without the discovery of fire; specific rituals could be viewed as cultural embellishments, but the structuring of the human family in some form was essential. So moral behavior and ethical codes, in that they attempt to guarantee social interaction and equilibrium, stand high in the hierarchical list of essentials for human survival.

It is this crucial position of ethics in human evolution, because their evolution is observable retrospectively in social institutions throughout history and currently in the efforts to regulate the forces of total destruction made possible by modern technological advances, that leads us to choose this product of psychosocial evolution for discussion.

The evolution of life in the biological sense is characterized by expediency. The maintenance, reproduction, diversification, and advancement of living forms in interaction with all existing environmental opportunities are its goal. It is therefore an entirely amoral process. If we derive man's psychosocial evolution out of a continuum with biological evolution, is it, too, amoral, guided by the principle of expediency and opportunism?

We raise this question in order to clarify a possible source of misunderstanding. That morality and ethics evolved for reasons of human survival and were in this sense expedient does not equate this process with the possible opportunistic content of a specific ethic in a given individual or group. We cannot make a value judgment simply on the basis of using the word "expediency" in different contexts, by attempting to compare two phenomena of an entirely different order, one the amoral evolution of life, the other, the moral or immoral behavior of individuals or groups in which factors of motivation are involved. We would be committing the same error made by the social Darwinists in taking the selection principle as a social good and applying "the survival of the fittest" as an apology for existing social ills, were we to deduce that a personal or group morality of expediency has its evolutionary justification.

On the other hand, a naive idealism should not deter us from seeing that expediency is not always a moral issue, that in its wake man evolved as a moral creature, and that it is often the catalyst, though neither inevitably nor exclusively, for advancement to higher levels of ethical conduct. A brief report on an interesting anthropological experiment,[3] the full implications of which the author did not at that time deduce, illustrates our point. Holmberg, in the course of an ethnological investigation of an exceedingly primitive aboriginal group of Indians in Eastern Bolivia, known as the Siriono, hit upon the idea of introducing them to a few items of technology with which they had had no previous contact. They were a seminomadic people, eking out a bare subsistence in the environment of a tropical forest, which provided them with neither stone nor metal. They depended, therefore, in the absence of all but wooden tools—a crude digging stick and a cumbersome bow and arrow—on hunting, fishing, collecting, and on the practice of some primitive agriculture in the natural clearings in the forest. In other words, they were a pre-Stone Age people, focused almost exclusively on obtaining sufficient food for survival. Into this economy, Holmberg introduced six machetes, six axes, and a small supply of rice and watermelon seed. This strikingly minimal introduction of technological items had a profound effect on these peoples, most obviously on their economic life, but as a consequence of this also upon their ego functions in terms of mastery, on their social interaction, and in some cases on their self-esteem as well.

Before the introduction of these artifacts, we note that the Siriono had manifested a great desire for superior technology, immediately upon making contact with the white men.* This is important evidence of the expansive impulses to achieve greater control of the environment even in a milieu whose limitations might be expected to have had a stultifying effect on personality—and within limits undoubtedly did. Nevertheless, their desire for technology was matched by the rapidity with which they learned to use the new tools: ". . . they progressed overnight from a technology of the pre-Stone Age to one of the Iron Age." What had taken a half day's work previously—the extracting of a palm cabbage, or of wild honey from a tree hollow—now, with the use of an ax, took less than an hour. "Wild fruits were more easily harvested; wood for bows and arrows and housebuilding was more readily extracted; slain animals were more rapidly cut up; mobility through swamp and jungle was greatly increased; wooden utensils and tools were better and more rapidly constructed. *In short, the productive capacity of the families receiving tools more than doubled at once.*"†

It is at this point that we are confronted with some of the major social effects of the introduction of the technological items. For budgetary reasons, their number was extremely limited, and they were, therefore, distributed only to a few families. It is important to bear in mind certain characteristics of the social background against which these changes took place. The Siriono are an extremely individualistic people; they did not co-operate in their small agricultural endeavors, nor, because of the great scarcity of food, were they ever inclined to share food outside the extended family. The

---

* Their only previous contact with white people had been with rubber tappers, or with mestizo farmers who lured them into working for them with promises of food and tools, only to exploit them in a position of servitude. Both encounters were of a hostile nature.

† Italics ours.

introduction, then, of technological implements that greatly increased the productive capacity of a limited few, was destined, in such a setting, to create social conflict. Holmberg notes and describes the great increase in in-group hostility and the jealous guarding of tools and produce.

From the standpoint of the evolution of ethics, we might be inclined to say that the Siriono are at a rather low level, showing little feeling for others and little capacity to share; and we might be tempted to conclude that their under-developed fellow feelings parallel their primitive economy and the scarcity of food. If we made such a judgment, how-ever, it would be measured against our own system of moral values. We are arguing here not for a relativistic view of moral values, in the sense that Siriono morality happens to be theirs and is, to them, "as good as" ours is for us; for we do indeed believe that the limitations in their capacity to identify with others place them at a lower hierarchical level in socio-cultural evolution (a point which we will explicate later); but we would make clear that the evolution of moral and ethical codes, like all products of evolution, have arisen to fit an existing situation. What is instructive in the social changes wrought by the introduction of tools to the Siriono should lead not to the exclamation: "How primitive their ethic!" but to the conclusion that whatever code they had evolved prior to the introduction of "technology" was ade-quate for their survival at that level, and that a change to a form of greater complexity and differentiation of social and economic organization necessitates a corresponding change in the complexity of ethical organization: or expressed more evolutionarily, creates the niche, the opportunity, for further ethical evolution. What Holmberg was witnessing when he observed with regret the increase in in-group hostility was a transitional period during which an imbalance existed between an economy that had advanced from its former position and the existing available ethic.

At the end of his report, Holmberg tells us that he has been informed by letter that "for the most part they [the Siriono] abandoned their old way of life, shifting from a largely nomadic to a largely settled existence based on agriculture." He then expresses his personal regret at having "had a hand in initiating some of the changes which probably ultimately overwhelmed them and over which neither I nor they had control." Whether the changes actually overwhelmed these particular people or not is, we feel, not the issue. From a sociocultural evolutionary point of view, we must assume that in principle peoples have the capacity to advance, that there are within groups exceptional individuals who become the foci around which change is structured, which then radiates throughout the total group, and that often the impetus for such change comes from contact with a more advanced culture. Holmberg's[4] basic faith in this capacity, although he may not express it in these terms, is illustrated in his very successful experiment in recent years with the Vicos Indians in Peru. Here, with some financial assistance in changing their economic situation and some instruction in modern agricultural methods, an entire group of individuals who had lived as serfs for generations were enabled to develop a democratic, co-operative, and relatively literate society within a few years. Such changes must have brought in their wake changes in ego processes, including greater feelings of competency, autonomy, and self-esteem, as well as new levels of relatedness to others and new cultural and ethical values. The latter, although not explicitly described as such by Holmberg, are implicit in the Vicos' ultimate, voluntary choice of a co-operative way of life.

In such examples, evolution shows us the meeting place

of social and psychological processes. A socioeconomic advance calls for new levels of ego organization, of which an ethical value system is an important part. Under the pressure of the new environmental niche, which represents an increase in socialization, man must draw upon his psychological resources to make the necessary adaptation in the form of a more advanced ethic. What is his major psychological resource in this area? It is the capacity to identify with and empathize with others, a capacity which is part of his native endowment—for his ability to structure ego is based upon it —and which is greatly reinforced in his earliest relationship with his mother in which he was the recipient, under normal conditions, of the mother's powerful empathic emotion and understanding.

What we term the capacity for empathy, which is a more or less consciously experienced and directed emotion toward another, and the concomitant capacity to co-operate with others, have a long evolutionary history in the animal kingdom, where they are not in the sphere of awareness, but where, perhaps for that very reason, their survival function is more apparent. Darwin[5] cites many interesting instances of communication and social interaction in higher animals which might be regarded as the precursors of human social reactions involving empathic responses. "The most common mutual service in the higher animals is to warn one another of danger by means of the united senses of all. . . . Rabbits stamp loudly on the ground with their hindfeet as a signal; sheep and chamois do the same with their forefeet, uttering likewise a whistle. Many birds, and some mammals, post sentinels. . . . Social animals mutually defend each other. Bull bisons in North America, when there is danger, drive the cows and calves into the middle of the herd, whilst they defend the outside. . . . Social animals perform many little services for each other: horses nibble, and cows lick each other, on any spot which itches; monkeys search each other for external parasites. . . . All animals living in a body, which defend themselves or attack their enemies in concert, must indeed be in some degree faithful to one another, and those that follow a leader must be in some degree obedient."

The ethologists refined these century-old yet accurate ideas of Darwin in their study of the social behavior of animals and showed that what Darwin refers to as "the united senses of all" is actually a system of interlocking releasers which controls the behavior patterns of animals in such a way as to release aggressive behavior toward predators and to inhibit it within the species, in the service of survival. What evolved as automatic, instinctual behavior patterns in animals fell within the domain of ego for man. Certainly, not all of man's social behavior is under conscious control in terms of the factors which motivate it. Many archaic impulses and unconscious by-products of repression play determining roles in motivating social interactions. Yet, the consummated social act is always conscious, as opposed to automatic. Nevertheless, the same issues are crucial to human as to animal survival, namely the control of aggressive feelings and actions within the species.

The problem of how the capacity to establish such controls evolved in the human species has both a phylogenetic and an ontogenetic aspect. It is also a part of the problem of the emergence of morality and ethics in man, seen from the side of the control of hostility rather than from the viewpoint of the ability to identify with another individual, which we have touched on earlier in this chapter. These two aspects of the question of morality and ethics are not only opposite vantage points, but are also interrelated and interacting.

An interesting hypothesis to explain the evolution of co-operative human interaction which would then create a basis for the cultivation of a moral sense in man is advanced by Berrill.[6] He associates the socialization of man in phylogenetic terms with his becoming a hunter of large game. Climatic changes which resulted in the formation of vast grasslands on the earth's surface and the subsequent evolution of the large herd animals, like the antelope and the horse, occupying this biosphere necessitated a co-operative kind of hunting if man was to survive on this game. The challenge of the new physical situation created selection pressure for those individuals most capable of meeting its requirements; one of these was the ability for social co-operation. Thus, Berrill asks: "Who did the hunting? Only those who were fast on their feet, nimble with their hands, quick to see and hear, and above all able to cooperate wholeheartedly with one another in the chase or trapping and capture of an animal. These lived, with all the more energy perhaps to repeat the performance. The dull of wit and uncooperative went hungry and left fewer progeny than the others to carry on the race. It was more important to obtain meat on the hoof than to take advantage of male lust or female heat or to indulge in vengeful anger on all other males. The future faded for those in whom the sex hormones continued to govern, but opened for those whose brains assumed an over-riding control of emotional reactions."

Whether this reconstruction is entirely accurate or not, it would seem in principle to approximate the reality that man, like all other animals, had to evolve controls over intraspecies hostility and ways of co-operating, communicating, and interacting socially in the interests of survival. Out of the enormous human reservoir created by individual differences, individuals who showed a capacity for socialization were those, who, through the operation of processes of natural selection, were destined to breed and survive. In the broadest phylogenetic sense then, we would look to some such process to account for man's socialization.

In the light of man's historical record of brutality and

savagery, of his difficulty in controlling aggressive behavior toward his fellow man in individual as well as in group encounters, and of the cataclysmic potentiality in present-day hostilities among nations which tend to threaten the total destruction of the species, coupled with the tendency in modern psychological thinking as it has been inspired by the psychoanalytic discovery of the importance of unconscious, emotional factors, to view man as driven by irrational forces, it is difficult to retain the broader evolutionary perspective which teaches us that the roots of socialization, and therefore ultimately of the capacity to love, constitute a preponderant part of man's archaic phylogenetic heritage. Furthermore, in the over-all, long term view of human sociocultural evolution, there has been an increase in the capacity for socialization, love, and empathy. As in the case of all evolutionary processes, the advance has not been consistently unilinear; there have been regressive and tangential developments, but in our view, the over-all movement has been progressive.

The question is so often asked: What accounts for man's social cohesion, or, in other words, what are the requisites for social behavior in *Homo sapiens?* The capacity for verbal symbolization and the use of language in communication, the ability to make tools of definite and standardized patterns, and the sociocultural transmission of information from one generation to another are some of the factors advanced as the crucial requisites for human social organization. Hallowell,[7] taking Jennings' view "that the foundation of any kind of social order is dependent upon role differentiation," considers this the crucial factor in human social organization, to which has been added man's capacity for a "normative orientation" that finds expression for values and goals in these social differentiations. While all of the above facts are phenomenologically true, can one, if one is thinking evolutionarily, legitimately ask what is the requisite for the evolution of any structure, social form, behavioral mode, or psychological entity? It seems to us that the question arises out of a tendency still to persist in deterministic causal thinking. In evolution, as a historical process, on the one hand, and as a future-directed one on the other (not in a finalistic sense, but in the sense of change and advance), each step in the hierarchy is as crucial as any other. Furthermore, in the highly complex, interactional unity of organism and environment, the emergence of new forms depends on such an intricately patterned and dynamically active system of variables that we cannot extract one factor and label it as requisite. The question, then, of man's capacity for socialization seems to be answered by the simple fact that he could only survive as a social creature. To this end, many factors played a role: for example, his neurophysiological development with the emergence of awareness, neotony, the development of memory and language, and the evolution of socio-cultural entities, such as artifacts, role differentiation, the human family, economic forms, and social traditions.

Upon the phylogenetically evolved capacity for socialization, man, through processes of identification, structured ego, capable of love and empathic relatedness on the one hand and adherence to social controls and requirements on the other. With the addition of the conscious awareness of these processes, the basis for moral and ethical behavior was given.

Psychoanalysis regards itself as biologically oriented, and as having "given us the first sound explanations of the ontogenesis of moral behavior."[8] Undoubtedly, the theory of super-ego formation as a process of psychic internalization growing out of the child's psychosexual conflicts within the familial matrix is a psychobiological theory of sorts. It rests on the recognition of the crucial factor of man's neotony, on the awareness of the strong affectional ties between the growing child and his parents, on what it regards as the universality of the incest taboo and the theory of childhood psychosexual development. However, the biological aspects of this theory are too narrow on several counts: first, in the attempt to derive the capacity for human moral behavior as a phylogenetic acquisition from an ontogenetic experience; second, limiting this experience to a sexual conflict; and third, by regarding only the restrictive aspects of morality. It derives the formation of the super-ego essentially from a theory of sexual anxiety: The male child at the height of his Oedipal strivings must forego sexual gratification with his mother for fear of punishment from the father in the form of castration; in a compensatory way, in order to preserve his own maleness and not to lose his father as a love object, he internalizes his image and with it all prohibitions and social controls. This internalized image becomes the core of an authority-bearing system within his personality which exerts pressure on the ego to inhibit instinctual gratification and to act in a socially acceptable way.

It seems to us that the positive contribution of this theory lies not in the content of the drive theory and of the psychosexual conflict which are at its root, but in the mechanism which it posits for the transmission of moral codes: the mechanism of internalization through processes of introjection and identification. For the phylogenetically acquired capacity for socialization must be represented in the minds of individuals as a concrete, patterned, and organized entity, and must be capable of being transmitted to succeeding generations to have social usefulness.

We would view the internalization of authority-bearing systems, as well as all that the child incorporates in terms of values, as the positive gains of introjection processes analogous to the acquisition of language and actually antedating it. If one observes in great detail the interaction between parents and small children in the preverbal stage of development, one realizes how much of "value system" the parent inadvertently communicates and how much the child absorbs. For example, the one-year-old who has just learned to walk and is attempting to negotiate a step down is helped by a solicitous parent with the encouraging admonition, "be careful," "slowly," "hold on"; or in his enthusiasm to pet the new puppy, he must be restrained with words such as "gently, gently," delivered in the quiet tone that conveys to the child the parent's awareness of the nature of the little animal as well as his understanding of the child's enthusiasm. Such small details convey a great deal to the child that later become part of his morality and finally of his ethic. He learns that he is loved and valued, that helpfulness is one way in which such feelings are acted upon, that care and gentleness are "virtues," and that living things are to be respected. Our illustration, of course, draws on a specific set of values characteristic for American culture and some parts of Europe. In principle, however, parents transmit their values, their moral and ethical codes, whatever their content, to their offspring in essentially the same manner: a manner which will obviously change as the developmental level of the child includes greater verbal comprehension.

The transmission of values which become the basis for moral behavior is much more than a system of commandments or deterrents of anti-social conduct. This is only one part of man's morality. For the rest, as a creature who has experienced his mother's empathic love, and later in human history, his father's, he learns to empathize with others and to structure within his own personality an organized set of moral principles which regulate his behavior and in terms of which he creates within society institutions that, in varying degrees, reflect this capacity.

Waddington,[9] a distinguished geneticist who is profoundly concerned with ethical problems, appreciates fully the important factor of "internalization" in man's socialization, and that there is a teacher, and one who is taught, in the role differentiation that makes up human society. However, his emphasis is on the authority-bearing nature of the teacher-pupil relationship, in its broadest sense, through which moral values are internalized. This would seem to us an over-emphasis on the factor of dominance and submission, as well as on the prohibiting and restricting aspect of morality. It tends to overlook the fact that internalization and identification take place on the basis of love and admiration as well and not exclusively as a result of anxiety. This tendency characterizes psychoanalytic thinking and results in a conception of personality in which the carrier of man's moral value system, his "normative orientation" as Hallowell calls it, is set apart from his ego in a more or less rigid structure known as the super-ego, which is antagonistic to the ego. Such a view has its origins in psychoanalytic concerns with pathology, in which, in certain personality types, notably the compulsive-obsessive neurosis or neurotic character, we encounter an overrigid morality in the form of a conscience which torments the ego relentlessly. The hypertrophy of a given aspect of personality should, however, not blind us to its proper place in normal human development.

We regard the moral and ethical values which man introjects in the course of his childhood as intricately interwoven with his total ego process, although identifiable as having certain specific content for the individual; furthermore, since the factor of love and empathy play at least an equal role with the fear of punishment for transgressions, in the internalization of values, there will be as much influence of ego-ideal as of super-ego on the values, morality, and ethics of man, i.e., they will be dominated as much by positive goals and strivings as by the restrictive character of commandments.

Here, we would agree with Suttie[10] who emphasizes maternal love as being of primary importance in the socialization of man.

In a morality based exclusively on coercion, there is no room for evolution. There can only be either increasingly acceptable rationalizations for the submission to authority or more efficient methods of enforcing it. But nothing changes essentially within man. He is left with the same untameable aggressive and destructive drives, which constantly seek discharge and must constantly be held down. Such, indeed, is the Freudian[11] view. On the other hand, a conception of social relatedness based on biological necessity and of a morality which grows out of it and is modeled after and tempered by affectional familial interactions, especially those of mother and child, leaves room for expansion, advance, and evolution. The opportunity for such advances lies in:

1. The variety and flexibility of loving interactions. These will differ in intensity and nature from one individual to another, as will the capacity to identify with the expression of love and tenderness. A vast psychosocial reservoir of individual differences in empathic capacity is thereby created, upon which social institutions can draw, as their evolution to increasingly complex forms will require greater empathic understanding of others.

2. Individual variability in the efficacy and autonomy of ego function, and the opportunities which society offers for its expression, which makes possible the implementation of morality in social action. Thus, a democratic, open-ended society will at one and the same time tend to produce individuals of greater ego autonomy and offer them greater opportunity for expressiveness than an authoritarian society or one whose social structure is extremely rigid. The evolution of moral codes is therefore more dynamic and more observable in such a society.

3. The psychological capacity of ego not only to internalize existing value systems, but also to synthesize out of a variety of experience and human contact new ego-ideals toward the realization of which it can then strive.

4. The dissemination of new ego-ideals through social institutions and their transmission from generation to generation through psychological mechanisms of identification.

We believe that ethical advance is observable throughout human history and is expressed in such monuments as the code of Hammurabi, the Dead Sea Scrolls, the Old and New Testaments, and the writings of Buddha; it is also reflected in institutions which have abolished slavery, or have protected the rights of citizens, or have respected the equality of women and the rights of children. The heroes which men create and admire, and whom they seek to emulate, mirror their ideals. These heroic images have changed in character throughout man's history and the changes, despite dramatically regressive trends, indicate a general advance in the capacity for empathic relatedness: From hunter to warrior, from the authoritarian figure of chieftain to that of absolute monarch, the trend goes in the direction of national and political leaders with whom men can identify as having come from their own ranks. The humanitarian personality of the nineteenth century and the scientist of today, to the extent that they are increasingly admired, are heroes whose values reflect increasing social awareness and a striving toward an empathic understanding of others.* We may say then that

---

* A keen and imaginative appreciation of the forward movement of the ethical aspect of socio-psychological evolution based on an advance and transmission of a changed ego-ideal is described by Teilhard de Chardin:[12]

"We can envisage a world whose constantly increasing 'leisure' and heightened interest would find their vital issue in fathoming everything, extending everything; a world in which giant telescopes and atom smashers would absorb more money and excite more spontaneous admiration than all the bombs and cannons put together; a world in which, not only for the

*the augmentation, throughout the evolutionary history of
ego, of the capacity for love and empathy, since it is critical
for man's survival and sociocultural evolution, becomes the
measure of the evolutionary level of his ethical systems.*

The question of the evolution of man's moral and ethical
values, even among scientists who are committed to a naturalistic approach to the problem, is a very controversial one.
There is a general reluctance, except for some notable
exceptions, to examine the principle of relativity in regard to
values and to set up some more or less absolute criteria for
advance in this area that would correspond to the progressive
hierarchy of evolution in the organic sphere. To some extent,
this is understandable in terms of the scientist's strict training
in objectivity and the resultant fear of the intrusion of a
subjective bias. Nowhere would it be easier to succumb to
subjective inclinations than in an evaluation of man's morality.
Yet, it should be possible to deal with man's evolved capacity
to structure value systems as part of his ego, without subscribing to, or judging, in terms of content, any particular
value system. This is Waddington's[9] approach when he writes:
"The human infant is born with probably a certain innate
capacity to acquire ethical beliefs but without any specific
beliefs in particular." This innate capacity is implemented,
through social interaction, in the creation of value systems
in the mind which show an evolutionary direction in the
course of human history: "Any particular set of ethical
beliefs, which some individual man may advance, can be
meaningfully judged according to their efficacy in furthering

---

restricted band of paid research-workers, but also for the man in the street,
the day's ideal would be the wresting of another secret or another force
from corpuscles, stars, or organised matter; a world in which, as happens
already, one gives one's life to be and to know, rather than to possess. That,
on an estimate of the forces engaged, is what is being relentlessly prepared
around us."

this general evolutionary direction." The direction is determined by "an improvement in the mechanism of formation and development of the super-ego as a part of the functional machinery of human evolution." Although not in complete agreement with Waddington regarding the mechanisms by which man's morality is acquired, we share with him and with Julian Huxley, whose conception of improvement we have discussed and who advances similar ideas in connection with ethics, the belief that man's morality is as much a subject for scientific investigation as is his neurophysiology, of which it is indeed an ultimate by-product. It is part of the evolutionary stream of life to which we attribute direction in terms of advance.

It is noteworthy that anthropologists, biologists, and psychologists who have been concerned with human sociocultural evolution do not hesitate to describe as "evolutionary" advance improvements in technology, mode of subsistence, social and economic organization, and even in art forms. But they generally eschew any dealing in evolutionary terms with processes of socialization and their expression in moral codes and ethical systems, even though these very things are reflected in the social institutions which they describe. If value judgments in terms of progress are to be avoided, why is a nomadic hunting culture regarded as more primitive, less advanced, than a settled agricultural society? The obvious answer lies in the increased complexity and permanence of organization of the latter which creates a greater number of environmental opportunities for the further evolution of the individuals within the society and of its social institutions. In other words, increasing complexity of social organization parallels similar processes in physical organization, in that it creates the opportunity, through a multiplication of the possible variety of interactions, for the emergence of something new. How is it possible to conceive of progress in social organization without corresponding advance in the psychological structures which are in constant reciprocal interaction with them? And since human morality is a vital part of these psychological processes, it too must increase in intricacy and complexity of psychological organization—an evolution which is reflected in all human institutions which either regulate social interaction or set up ideals for man's social achievement.

Scientists who see an incompatibility between science and moral values are often caught up in an inability to divorce the *capacity* on man's part for ethical behavior from a specific ethic in terms of content. Thus, Gillespie[13] writes: "For neither in public nor in private life can science establish *an* ethic.* It tells what we can do, never what we should. Its absolute incompetence in the realm of values is a necessary consequence of the objective posture." As confirmation of his point of view, Gillespie quotes from an essay of Henri Poincaré on "Morality and Science":

"It is not possible to have a scientific ethic. . . . If the premises of a syllogism are both in the indicative, the conclusion will equally be in the indicative. In order for the conclusion to be put in the imperative, it would be necessary for at least one of the premises to be in the imperative. Now, the principles of science, the postulates of geometry, are and can only be in the indicative—at the foundations of science there is not, cannot be, anything else. . . . The most subtle dialectician . . . will never obtain a proposition which says: do this, or do not do that; that is to say, a proposition which confirms or contradicts ethics."

The nodal point of confusion in what, on the face of it, seems to be a statement of exceeding clarity, lies in the identification of ethics with an *imperative* proposition. Certainly, specific ethical codes are stated in the imperative and certain

---

* Italics ours.

internalized psychological mechanisms carry some imperative character: notably, the psychoanalytic conception of the super-ego. Yet, the imperative by no means covers all that is moral or ethical in man. A mother's empathic love for her child; that human beings and their animal ancestors before them communicate and co-operate with one another and that this fact has, through evolution, become part of human awareness as well as part of internalized psychic structure; that the nature of such co-operation has changed in a positive directional way, although not by any means consistently; that human beings create, out of the social fabric, ego-ideals to which they aspire and that these, too, have changed—these are *indicative* propositions from which the capacity for moral conduct and its evolution can be deduced.

Furthermore, the validity of scientific observations cannot be judged by whether they can be reduced to syllogisms or not. Such reduction would describe only one level of scientific inquiry which permits of linear causal thinking. In attempting to understand processes such as evolution, and especially human sociocultural evolution, which involve an intricacy of interactional systems operating through time in a directional manner, one must strive to apprehend the unifying principles in the pattern of the total phenomenon. This does not lend itself to thinking on the syllogistic level.

The question of ethics and evolution has much to gain from a broad historical approach which seeks not to evaluate a particular ethic, either of individual or limited group, but to grasp the ethos of an era. This ethos, as a more or less stabilized system of values and ego-ideals running through a human population of a given period, can be used as one important indicator of the ego evolutionary level of the period. In describing the guiding ideas that permeate his work, George Sarton,[14] the great historian of science, refers to the need for toleration and charity. He does so not out of romantic idealism (although only a person of his ethical stature could have drawn such lessons from history), but because the hard lessons of human history demonstrate the futility, in terms of sociocultural evolution, of intolerance, bigotry, autarchy: "Intolerance is always destructive, not only of its natural and immediate victims, but of the oppressors themselves. . . . The church was ever ready to persecute dissenters, not only among laymen, but even more among its own clerics. A long series of books were burned and men imprisoned or murdered during the fourteenth century. . . . Even if one accepts the abominable doctrine that the end justifies the means, those crimes were not justified, for they did not attain their very purpose. They did not save the offenders, but doomed to eternal punishment the persecutors. They did not save the church, but increased its peril and paved the way for the Reformation. In a long view, nothing is more certain than the uselessness of persecution." In citing another example, Sarton speaks of the history of Spain and shows that the increasingly violent and efficient persecution of so-called heretics resulted finally in the material and spiritual ruin of their country. "In spite of that colossal failure, their methods have been imitated in our own times in other countries of Europe; it is not necessary to be a prophet to foretell with almost complete certainty that the final result will be the same as in Spain, to wit, self-destruction. . . .

"Science is unable to teach us toleration and charity, but the history of science (e.g. in the fourteenth century) gives us inductive proof of their need."

The historical predictability of self-destructive consequences resulting from the violation of certain fundamental ethical principles in human social interaction would not be possible if these principles were not indeed fundamental. The inevitable ethic of empathic love and understanding which

Sarton derives from history is the same which we derive from the evolution of man's consciousness, the nature of his social interactions, and the psychic internalization of his social world.

For Sarton the history of science "is an account of definite progress, the only progress clearly and unmistakably discernible in human evolution. Of course, this does not mean that scientific progress is never interrupted. There are moments of stagnation and even regression here or there; but the general sweep across the times and across the countries is progressive and measurable. The history of science includes the most glorious, the purest, and the most encouraging deeds in the whole past."[14]

Perhaps, the historical progress of science is more tangible than that of other human endeavors; yet, we feel that man's sociocultural evolution, despite many regressions, shows a generally progressive trend, which includes his ethical strivings. The profundity of Sarton's understanding of this fact, although not explicitly stated, is implicit in his conception of the function of the historian in the very process of furthering ethical evolution. Thus, he writes: "Great scientific achievements are rare, great men of science are rarer still. It is important to describe their greatness when it occurs, and thus *create noble emulations.** The lives of such men as Faraday, Darwin, Pierre and Marie Curie deserve to be studied as the lives of saints, saints of a new kind, new models for the youth of today. It is the historian of science's duty to draw the portraits of those great leaders, and to hold them up for remembrance, gratitude, and devotion. In this way he continues and fulfills the old tradition of history as a mirror. It is his business to polish the mirror and to watch it as jealously as the astronomer watches his own mirrors. These

---

* Italics ours.

reflect the stars, the historian's mirror reflects man."[14]

Intuitively, Sarton perceives the psychological fact which we have described above that man's psychosocial evolution, especially in the area of ethics, proceeds not only by the social transmission of codes, but also by the operation of those creative ego processes which synthesize new ego-ideals, and by their transmission and dissemination throughout a population.

■ REFERENCES

1. Huxley, J. S.: Evolution, cultural and biological. *Current Anthropology*. University of Chicago Press, Chicago, 1956, pp. 3-25.
2. Bidney, D.: *Theoretical Anthropology*. Columbia University Press, New York, 1953.
3. Holmberg, A. R.: Adventures in culture change. In Spencer, R. F., Ed.: *Method and Perspective in Anthropology*. University of Minnesota Press, Minneapolis, 1954.
4. Holmberg, A. R.: Miracle at Vicos. *Reader's Digest*. April, 1963.
5. Darwin, C.: *The Descent of Man*. Random House, Modern Library, New York, 1936, pp. 474-476.
6. Berrill, N. J.: *Man's Emerging Mind*. Dodd, Mead & Co., New York, 1955.
7. Hallowell, A. I.: Self, society and culture. In Tax, S., Ed.: *The Evolution of Man, Evolution After Darwin*, Vol. II. University of Chicago Press, Chicago, 1960, pp. 309-371.
8. Hartmann, H.: *Psychoanalysis and Moral Values*. International Universities Press, New York, 1960.
9. Waddington, C. H.: *The Ethical Animal*. Atheneum, New York, 1961, pp. 7, 26, 157, 174.
10. Suttie, I. D.: *The Origins of Love and Hate*. Kegan Paul; Trench, Trubner & Co., Ltd., London, 1935.

11. Freud, S.: *Civilization and Its Discontents*. Doubleday, New York, 1958.
12. Teilhard de Chardin, P.: *The Phenomenon of Man*. Harper & Row, New York, 1959, pp. 279-280.
13. Gillespie, C. C.: *The Edge of Objectivity*. Princeton University Press, Princeton, N. J., 1960, pp. 154-155.
14. Sarton, G.: *Sarton on the History of Science*, Essays selected and edited by Dorothy Stimson. Harvard University Press, Cambridge, 1962, pp. 19-20, 21, 63.

13 · THE THERAPEUTIC UNDERTAKING
IN EVOLUTIONARY PERSPECTIVE

As THE MACROCOSM of the solar system is reflected in the microcosm of the atom, so the broad outlines of psycho-social evolution are reflected in the psychotherapeutic encounter between two individuals. It is precisely because all the manifestations of life's processes form one evolutionary continuum that we are justified in relating and attempting to integrate the observations of a specific phenomenon to a more general whole, and conversely in applying knowledge of the laws and interrelationships of the totality to the limited observation.

In the therapeutic situation, we have the unique opportunity to observe change in the psychological life of an individual. We do not mean only change in the sense of recovery from psychic illness or maladaptation, although such change may or may not have evolutionary implications. Mirrored in the personality of the individual, in his motivations, self-image, moral and ethical codes, strivings toward self-realization, and in the nature of his interaction with others is the psychosocial evolutionary level of his generation as it may mark some change from that of his immediate forebears. Added to this are the changes which his own individuality, i.e., constitutional predispositions and individual life history, have wrought within his particular personality as contrasted with others of his time, as well as within the social milieu in which he functions.

Certainly, not all change is advance. Nevertheless, it has been the observation of change in the form of the individual's striving toward higher levels of integration and expressiveness that caused us to regard this phenomenon, and the impetus which propelled it, as an aspect of evolution as a whole, and to search out that characteristically human feature which is the vehicle of man's psychosocial evolution. This search led us to review the hierarchical development of organic evolution to its most complex form, man, and to find in the extraordinary evolution of his brain and nervous system that bridge between the organic and the psychological which was to call for the emergence of consciousness and its organizing principle, ego. In ego, we see the instrument of psychosocial evolution, which feeds back to this very instrument the materials from which ego evolution itself proceeds.

Thus, the psychotherapeutic situation afforded us an evolutionary perspective on ego; such a perspective had inevitably to change certain aspects of our conception of personality and of our therapeutic task.

In the pre-Freudian period, in which psychology was dominated by the philosophy of rationalism, human behavior was regarded only from the standpoint of conscious action, reaction, and motivation. Freud's discoveries extended the area of observation into depth and demonstrated the existence of unconscious factors as additional motivating and determining forces in human behavior.

These discoveries came through a study of conflict as manifested in various forms of psychopathology. The difference between the normal and the neurotic was thought to be only one of degree, and the findings derived from the observation and treatment of neurotics was applied to a psychology of normal personality structure. While much that emerged in this manner does indeed describe normal functioning and normal development, the derivation of Freudian psychology from the abnormal left its mark on a theory of personality in the form of a regressive conception of human motivation, indeed of life itself. Freud saw man as largely driven by unconscious instinctual impulses, the gratification of which constituted his main motivation. Man's striving was not progressive, expansive, but instinctual, regressive. In these strivings, he was hindered by the demands of society: his ego being caught between these demands and those of his own impulses.

Although trained and educated originally in this school of thought, modifications which had several points of origin appeared in our thinking and in our therapeutic procedures. We began to be impressed by the expansive wish for self-realization on the part of patients and to learn that the uncovering of unconscious impulses, the recovery of childhood amnesias, and the reliving of early affective experiences did not in themselves inevitably bring about this self-realization. In two specific areas of particular interest to us, Freudian theory seemed inadequate, nonbiological, and sociologically unsound.

One was the study of the repetition compulsion and moral masochism, for which the Freudian recourse to a death instinct (a regressive drive toward a nonliving state) seemed, as an explanation, to contradict all that we know of life's adaptive capacities. The crucial question as to the survival function of this seemingly destructive mechanism had not been asked; once we asked it, the possibility for explaining human behavior in broader evolutionary terms was opened up.[1, 2]

Similarly, the Freudian conception of the development of the female personality structure was equally nonbiological and also failed to qualify its findings with reference to the social framework in which its observations were made. Perhaps no single clinical observation served as convincingly to confirm our impression that the human ego was on the evolutionary move as the ego advance of modern woman in the framework of an open-ended society, as we viewed this in historical perspective.

Gradually, we began to see human behavior—whether in the personal interactions of individuals or on the larger social scene—as part of the evolutionary life stream and to view the human ego both as the expression of this evolutionary force and as the vehicle for its further advance. This new vantage point opened the way, gradually and unconsciously at first, but later with more conscious awareness, to the creation of a new kind of therapeutic encounter.

It would be valuable in attempting to clarify our points of view regarding personality and psychotherapy to juxtapose them with a brief review of the essential features of the Freudian model of personality. This model, as did our own, grew largely out of observations made in a psychotherapeutic situation. The emphasis was on the affective life of the individual and on conflict between opposing impulses as these are reflected in varying parts or processes of the personality.

Thus, although Freudian thought has changed within its own historical development, the idea of *conflict*—whether between conscious and unconscious, between Id and Ego, or Ego and Super-ego—is central to its conception of the neuroses from which it derives its conception of personality as well as its therapeutic procedures. This is manifest even in recent psychoanalytic writings according to which motivation and psychic organization are seen primarily as the outcome of conflict and defensive struggles.[3] Human motivation toward thought and action is derived entirely from the necessity to reduce the inner tensions created by the pressure of instinctual drives.[4] Thus, according to Freud[5] the energy system that is the human organism seeks through the consistent reduction of tension not only to achieve a state of equilibrium but tends as well to regress to earlier developmental levels. The process of maturation is seen then as a continuous struggle against such regressive forces which are finally victorious in that the organism succumbs to death.

Although the concept of a death-instinct as a systematic part of personality theory appears relatively late in Freudian theory, it cannot be dismissed or encapsulated from the main body of theory merely as a speculative hypothesis, since it is the logical end-product of a regressive conception of personality, indeed of life itself.

The concepts of progression or regression have validity only in relation to a point of reference. One advances beyond a given point in a space-time continuum or moves backward from it. In Freudian theory, the frame of reference is the developmental sequence of qualitatively changing phases of the instinctual life, known as "libido theory."[6] The well-known oral, anal, phallic, and genital phases normally appear sequentially in the emotional development of the individual, color the nature of object relationships, of character, of the quality of ego defenses, and of ego functioning, and represent the framework against which the regression, fixation, or progression of the personality is measured. It is not difficult to see that because these concepts have their origin in a concern with pathology and its treatment and the goal of development is conceived as the achievement of mature genitality, they tend to become a value system in which regression and progression can become value judgments. Against this background of instinctual forces which tend to draw the organism back to an earlier state of being, the embattled ego seeks to mediate adaptation to inner and outer environment.

It is true, as mentioned above, that contemporary writers[7] in the field of psychoanalytic theory grant an area of independence to the ego, both in terms of genesis and developmental function. There are then innate ego functions, the potentiality for which are present from birth, which unfold as the organism matures and which belong to a "conflict-free ego sphere." However, the term "conflict-free" implies through its very dichotomy the maintenance of the original frame of reference: the vicissitudes of the reservoir of instinctual energy as the wellspring which determines the differentiation and formation of most ego structure and function, and as the measuring rod for ego regression or progression.*

Such a view disregards the implications of the broadest phylogenetic, evolutionary framework within which human consciousness arose as the highest expression of nervous system adaptation, and from which the imperative for ego as the integrator of consciousness arose. Within such a framework the primacy of ego as an evolutionary derivative of consciousness remains unchallenged by the existence of other forces either within the organism or in the external environment. Its regression or progression is measured not against a developmental background of instinctual drives which are

---

* Dissatisfaction with this formulation led White recently to posit independent ego energies.[8]

considered primary and which have a finite goal in personality development, but in evolutionary terms according to its ability to synthesize and integrate the forces of inner and outer environment. The implication is that such integrative processes function in an open system giving rise to an infinite variety of adaptive and expansive possibilities. The origin, development, and function of ego thus parallels the life process itself in that its very existence and persistence is guaranteed by its capacity to evolve.

As a product of phylogeny, then, ego has emerged through evolutionary pressure and has become the carrier of its sociopsychological form as reflected in culture, which in turn influences the further qualitative evolution of ego itself.

It is important to bear this in mind, for culture, in the structural and functional nature of its social dimension as expressed in its laws, religion, and moral and ethical codes, does not only create value systems and perpetuate these in the form of prohibitions, commands, and ideologies, but provides the opportunity for the formation of basic identifications within the family and in an open-ended society for transcending these in the larger social sphere. It thereby provides nutriment for ego formation and influences the nature and quality of ego directly.

Ego as the psychological representative of the integrative function of the nervous system is at the core of personality: primary, in the sense that at every point in development its nature reflects the synthesis of its endogenous neural substratum and its record of past experience, with its current action in, and reaction to, environment.* It is thus changing and further structuring itself within the developmental dimension of the individual, and effecting evolutionary change within a population through its interaction with culture. Ego

---

* Cf. Chapter VII.

is not a secondary derivative of interactions of other aspects of the personality, e.g., instinctual impulses, with environment, but is that synthesized quality of awareness through which all else is experienced. Ego represents the continuity of what the individual *is* in all the dimensions of space and time.

The progressive, primary, and active conception of ego, which derives from an evolutionary perspective, inevitably leads to a specific emphasis in the perception of personality, which parallels this conception and a corresponding modification in approach in dealing with it psychotherapeutically.

When an individual makes the decision to undergo a psychotherapeutic procedure, he is moved not solely by an awareness of "illness," and unhappiness and the wish for help with the resolution of neurotic conflict in the exclusively passive or even magical sense of that term, but in *varying degrees* by an active wish to alter his self-conception as this reflects his total functioning, self-expression, and introspection. In Chapter VIII, we have described this aspect of the patient's motivation as stemming from the ego's synthesizing and integrating tendencies as these obtain their momentum from the evolutionary thrust of life, of which ego itself is a derivative. In subjective terms, this is often experienced as a wish for mastery of oneself, for fulfillment of one's potentialities, or in Rogers'[9] terms, of "self-actualization." As such, it is an impulse toward optimal individuation through the seeking out of a new experience that hopefully will provide new focal points, whether they are models for identification or new values around which a resynthesis of ego processes can take place.

The individual patient seen in evolutionary perspective is then a part of the dynamic, ongoing processes of sociocultural evolution, especially as these exist in an open-ended society in transition. His failures in the adequate, adaptive synthesis of his personality are not due exclusively to anomalies in his ontogenetic development, whether psychosexual or psychosocial, but in many instances to the complex interaction of psychosocial with individual evolutionary processes. His ego is called on to integrate original identifications with new functions and ideals that are in part the product of the dynamically creative societal process which opens up new niches for ego expansion—even though such societal changes, at a given point in time, may not always represent positive developments in the direction of advance. That ego is called on and is striving through its integrative function to reach new levels of synthesis within a societal framework that is itself in evolutionary movement is one of the sources of anxiety as well as of guilt for which the patient seeks psychotherapeutic help.

However, it should be remembered, especially in regard to the task of creating a productive therapeutic climate, that the fruits of psychosocial evolution as they are manifested, for example, in the open-ended society of the United States, and are reflected in the individual ego, are not predominantly negative, as Erikson [10] has pictured them—i.e., as evidence of restlessness and lack of tradition which fosters faulty identifications and therefore faulty ego development. Rather, they offer positive opportunities for the expansion of ego functions, for greater ego autonomy, and for the greater development of individual potentiality. The therapist's appreciation of this positive aspect of individual ego striving for higher levels of integration despite accompanying anxiety or guilt is a major contribution of an evolutionary viewpoint. It implements the optimistic assumption that the ego will find whatever resources it needs for its resynthesis, growth and expansion, if it can perceive the therapist's belief in the existence of such resources. In this aspect of the therapeutic interaction, we hear an echo of the normal mother's love for her child which on one level is expressed in a belief in his inevitable growth: a belief whose anticipatory nature actually promotes development as described in Chapter IX.

Without placing their thinking within the framework of evolution, a number of therapists have perceived the importance of understanding the patient's striving toward ego expansion with the corresponding structuring of the therapeutic situation as one in which a new experience will serve to facilitate this end.

Thus, Schonbar[11] describes a transitional period in treatment during which the patient has modified his behavior on the basis of using the therapist or the therapist's expectations as a model. However, to interpret only the regressive, transference aspects of this behavior would be to deny the forward movement that is implicit in the change, even though it has as yet not been fully consolidated into the patient's own independent ego. Concerning this Schonbar writes:

"This is the same process he [the patient] went through in his initial socialization, save that the basis for the expectation was different. To interpret this bit of behavior *solely* in terms of his need for an authority would be damaging, for it would ignore the *incipient positive movement* involved. Its importance is not so much in the fact that it reveals that the analyst is having some impact on the patient, but that the patient is searching *ahead* of himself in reaction and is using the image of the therapist to enable himself to do so."*

The therapeutic significance of the therapist's emotional responsiveness to the patient's struggle for what we would term a higher level of ego integration is most sensitively expressed by Weigert:[12]

"The active sympathy of the psychotherapist in differentiation from a passive empathy is not only a transference phe-

---

* Italics ours.

nomenon; it is a part of this value enhancing love, capable of envisioning the personality of the patient in his potential wholeness, even though this wholeness may at present be adumbrated by a preponderance of destructive processes from which the patient seeks liberation."

We have already described the effect of an evolutionary perspective on an understanding of the patient's motivation toward treatment: that some aspect of this may in many cases and in varying degrees be inspired by the tendency of ego to seek opportunities for its own evolutionary advance. Such a view automatically defines an aspect of the therapist's role, i.e., to provide this opportunity in the social interaction that is the therapeutic encounter. While it undoubtedly is important to clear the way for an optimal interaction between patient and therapist by uncovering repressed impulses where these have interfered with ego synthesis in the course of development, it is equally important to realize that the key to therapeutic effectiveness, and growth, lies in the quality of the new experience of relatedness between two individuals. Thus, the actualization of ego function takes place in terms of interrelationship.

A number of authors have been aware of this fact and have described it in varying terms. They have not seen its evolutionary implications,* nor have they described it as an ongoing psychological process within the larger framework of psychosocial evolution. As early as 1935, Ian D. Suttie,[18] in reaffirming Ferenczi's dictum, "The physician's love heals the patient," carried the concept further in the conclusion "that the essential process in psychotherapy is to offer the patient the means of re-establishing free feeling-interest relationships with his

---

* Rogers[9] in acknowledging "that the substratum of all motivation is the organismic tendency toward fulfillment" is expressing an evolutionary viewpoint, which, however, is not explicitly described as such nor is it systematized.

social environment in the person of the analyst to begin with."

It is understandable that in these relatively early days in the history of psychoanalysis, Suttie expresses the goals of therapy in terms of "feeling," rather than in terms of ego integration. The importance of his contribution, however, lies in his awareness that the patient's betterment depends on the creation of an opportunity for a new experience in a loving interaction with the therapist.[14-15] Otto Rank,[16] who was certainly a pioneer in his concern with the reality of the patient-therapist relationship, emphasized the importance of the new experience as a curative factor. He wrote: "The patient reacts, it is true, with his old, typical patterns, as psychological theory in part commonly presents them, but he reacts to a new situation which in its ethical aspects constitutes the peculiarly constructive therapeutic agent." The term "ethical" has specific meaning for Rank, as his translator and co-worker, Jessie Taft, explains: "'Ethical' as used by Rank in contrast to 'moral' refers to the inherent and inevitable relation of the self to the other. Ethics, unlike morality, is not man-made, but the result of an inescapable reciprocal relationship beginning with the biological tie to the mother."

In Rank's thinking there is implied the same parallel between the desirable climate of the therapeutic encounter and the early mother-child relationship of which we spoke above.

A validation and extension of this point of view comes from Carl R. Rogers[17] whose observations of the psychotherapeutic process lead him to posit as crucial factors to the patient's developmental change, and therefore for the actualizing of his ego functions, first "an accurate and sensitive empathy communicated by the therapist," second, "a warmth of positive regard for the client," third, "the unconditionality of the therapist's regard," fourth, "the congruence of the therapist," by which is meant his own level of what we would call ego integration, and fifth, the capacity of the patient to perceive these qualities in the therapist, at least to a minimal degree. Thus, "personality change is a function of certain measured relationship qualities."

The biological basis for the possibility of such a therapeutic effect rests on three major and interdependent premises: first, that the evolutionary potential resides in ego, the psychological precipitate of central nervous system evolution and the carrier of psychosocial evolution; second, that ego is structured in a social matrix—initially in the environment of the mother-child relationship; and third, that the therapeutic milieu can create on a new and advanced level the productive aspects of that early relationship in the service of restructuring and resynthesizing ego processes. Suttie, DeForest, Storr, Rogers, and Rank are among those authors who openly stress the importance of self-realization and fulfillment of optimal potentiality as therapeutic goals for the patient and see the model for the therapeutic climate and interaction that will bring this about in the mother-child relationship.

An acknowledgment of the impetus of ego toward new interactions which will facilitate the optimal realization of its normal functions, and in many cases toward creative expression which outreaches these functions, leads us to emphasize in therapy the "real" and "actual" relationship of therapist and patient and to view as but one element those aspects of the relationship which are echoes of the past, i.e., which are the projected derivatives of the patient's emotional history and which are known as the "transference." This does not mean that it is unimportant to make the patient aware of the distortions in perception, reaction, and behavior in relation to the therapist that are the outgrowth of early, repressed, and still unconscious conflicts.[19, 20]* On the contrary, such an analysis of the past, reflected in the transference relationship,

---

* In Sullivan's[21] writings, these phenomena are referred to as parataxic distortions.

clears the ground for the setting up of the new relationship in the framework of which the evolutionary forces in personality can come into play. Thus, a new learning situation is created, in which new experiences, identifications, emotions, and ideals can become synthesized by ego at a new level of functioning.* The enlargement of the sphere over which ego has control cannot depend solely on the extension of consciousness to that which was previously unconscious, but must include the incorporation of newly experienced relationships and interactions.

The resynthesis of ego is inevitably accompanied by anxiety. This is not neurotic anxiety, but the normal reaction of the organism to an untried function, and calls for a special approach on the part of the therapist. Here, the real nature of his activity would do well to coincide with the maternal role in allaying anxiety, by mediating through explanation, understanding, patience, and confirmation between the patient's tentative attempts to test out new ways of reacting and reality itself. The ego's need and search for confirmation cannot be overestimated. It is the unavoidable by-product of the pressures for growth and evolutionary change to which ego is subject. As an example, we can point to the fact that an important aspect of the evolution of ego is manifested in the individual's attempt to synthesize advanced ego-ideal elements with aspects of the original ego-ideal derived from the relationship to parents.† In this synthesis, something new and individual has evolved which varies from or exceeds the model and which therefore precipitates some anxiety or guilt. To reduce this anxiety by a confirmation of the ego-ideal in

---

* A similar emphasis is made by Jung[18] when he writes, "My aim is to bring about a psychic state in which my patient begins to experiment with his own nature—a state of fluidity, change and growth, in which there is no longer anything eternally fixed and hopelessly petrified."

† Cf. Chapter X.

the new relationship with the therapist is the patient's legitimate need in therapy. It should become the therapist's function, regardless of whether, in content, the ego-ideal corresponds to his own or not.

The ability to communicate such confirmation of the patient's ego at every point in its reintegrative attempts and profoundly to respect its individuality calls for great maturity, integration, and plasticity on the part of the therapist's own ego. For him to contribute to the patient's ego advance through the social interaction that is the therapeutic encounter, his own ego must, at least in some respects that are significant for the patient, be on a higher evolutionary level of integration than that of the patient. Only in this way can he be, in part at least, a model for the new identifications that are the vehicles of sociocultural evolution.

The optimal integration of ego function is the general goal of therapy. Within the frame of reference of psychosocial evolution this can be described as:

1. The capacity for the development of maximal relatedness, i.e., love.

2. The ability to take action and to make choices without undue anxiety or guilt. This includes inner psychic action, i.e., thought and contemplation, as well as overt behavior.

3. The capacity for sufficient flexibility to adjust to societal change, which may be of an evolving nature.

4. The ability to develop individuation and to tolerate it when it differs from prevailing societal mores.

5. The ability to evolve maximal expressiveness and to search out that societal niche which will be most furthering of these potentialities.

6. The ability to express those healthy aspects of willing which are an outgrowth of the evolutionary striving of ego and to give up willing when it is perceived as unproductive

to these ends, i.e., to be appropriately active and passive, to strive, and to accept limitations.*

7. The capacity for enjoying the life processes, for being versed in the "art of living," for acknowledging its playful and aesthetic aspects.[23]

8. The ability to perceive and place one's individual life within the larger context of evolution as a whole, especially of its sociopsychological dimension.

These are obviously ideal goals of therapy which can only be approximated. But it might be valuable to examine some of the obstacles to their realization. One lies in the deterministic thinking of the classical psychoanalytic therapist and its effect on the ego of the patient. An interpretation of behavior, attitude, or feeling on the part of the patient which is derived from exclusively straight-line causal thinking not only disregards the fact that any behavior is the product of a complex, dynamic "patterned process" containing a great number of interacting variables, and thereby distorts the truth, but also violates the ego of the patient by imposing upon him, from a position of authority, the necessity for accepting a partial truth as the whole one. Deterministic thinking and the authoritative stance reinforce each other and create a static atmosphere in the therapeutic situation which interferes with the free interaction between therapist and patient, thus inhibiting the growth of the patient's ego to higher levels of integration.†

---

* For a detailed study of the psychology of "Willing" and its implementation in psychotherapy, we refer the reader to Milton Mazer[22] and to Otto Rank's[16] *Will Therapy and Truth and Reality*, especially to Chapter II, "The Basis of a Will Therapy," pp. 7-19.

† Speaking of the freedom for new levels of integration which the therapy should offer the patient, Edith Weigert writes: "In order to experience such a liberation, therapists and patients cannot remain strict adherents of a philosophy of absolute determinism. Both must have a faith to some degree in freedom of choice, alteration of decisions, commitment and responsibility in relation to values that have a super-personal meaning."[12]

An illustration of the application of a theory of straight-line causality is the overevaluation of childhood experience as responsible for the neuroses—for character in general as a matter of fact. Certainly, childhood experience is one vector in a pattern of causality relative to the formation of the adult personality. Yet, constitutional factors, including the strength of the instinct life and the nature of ego, as well as the socio-cultural framework, which is in flux and is interacting with the changing experiences of the individual's life cycle, must also be accepted as part of causality. Failing this in psycho-therapy, the patient tends to project the responsibility for his difficulties exclusively on his parents and childhood experiences, thereby absolving himself of the task and depriving himself of the opportunity of mobilizing his ego energies for the structuring and progress of his own life.

Another obstacle in the pathway of the fulfillment of therapeutic goals is that specific and inevitable anxiety in the patient which reaches for its origins beyond his individual development to the very nature of the processes of psycho-social evolution. Let us take as an example the evolution throughout human history of man's sense of time. As a result of biological evolution, time has become part of man's conscious experience.* But because of the very existence of consciousness, of its possibilities for change and expansion through the integrating function of ego, the sense of time, as an aspect of psychological evolution, has evolved according to the level of scientific knowledge, the development of technology, and the socioeconomic structure characteristic of any given period in history. For instance, the replacement of the concept of eternity by the mathematical concept of infinity calls for new and higher levels of adaptation in the ego's orientation to reality. Automation, which has created

---

* Cf. Chapter IV.

a new sense of time, has produced pressure for evolutionary change in that the loss of certain gratifications in natural and social experience and of certain ego functions must be compensated for by new levels of awareness and a resynthesis of existing experience as well as an expansion into new functions. The new levels of ego adaptation which are thus called for inevitably produce anxiety.

It is part of the therapeutic task to deal with this anxiety, not merely as an ontogenous conflict of the patient, but as part of the phylogeny of man. The patient should have the opportunity of identifying with the therapist's evolutionary view of life which accepts some anxiety and unhappiness as a normal part of life and which sees the full implications of man's acquisition of conscious awareness. For it is through this evolutionary step that man has lost some of the immediacy of experience, even of the experience "I am," since all experience is filtered through the symbolic representation of his consciousness. This is not a metaphysical problem, but a psychobiological fact. To balance this loss, however, man has the unique opportunity to use his evolving awareness and evolving ego to achieve greater understanding and mastery of the world, of himself, of human relationships, and of gaining satisfaction from the fullest realization of these potentialities.

We have placed a heavy burden on the therapeutic encounter. Yet, as a goal we would not settle for less. Nevertheless, in evaluating what any given therapy is or what we think it should be, it is sobering to remember the nature of the dimensions we would measure. We are dealing with one social process, the psychotherapeutic relationship, having a potential for psychological evolution all its own, which is superimposed upon the larger sociocultural evolutionary process. As soon as we isolate one of these dimensions from the other in an attempt to characterize them accurately, we necessarily distort some aspect of the truth. The ontogenous and phylogenous aspects of psychosocial evolution with its biological basis are aspects of a total process. We must be aware that when we isolate any part of this totality for our consideration, even though such procedures have their justification, we create a condition analogous to Heisenberg's uncertainty principle in physics,[24] whereby the position and momentum of an electron cannot be observed simultaneously without distortion.

Before leaving the issue of psychotherapy as a delimited aspect of psychosocial evolution, we would ask the question: What, if any, is the role of psychotherapy in the evolution of ethics?

The therapeutic situation, in its organized, professional, and structured aspect is in itself a new manifestation of sociocultural evolution. There were, of course, throughout human history, psychotherapeutic relationships more formally expressed in the functioning of the priesthood and later in medicine, and more informally in the interaction of teacher and pupil, of elders and youth, of friends with one another. However, as a separate professional entity, the psychotherapist is new on the human scene. That his existence is the answer to a need caused by the prevalence of mental and emotional disturbances, which in themselves are consequences of certain aspects of sociocultural evolution, is a complex aspect of the problem, the treatment of which would be a digression from the theme of this book. Nevertheless, the existence of some systematized knowledge of personality and its disturbances, and its implementation in a psychotherapeutic relationship, has created the opportunity for a new human experience: new as a cultural manifestation in evolutionary terms, new for therapist and patient alike, new in the uniqueness of each therapeutic encounter.

For the therapist, the responsibility of helping another

human being in the most subjective aspect of his life necessitates his drawing upon much more than psychological knowledge; he must approach the patient with all the empathic understanding at his command.* A relationship modeled in its emotional climate after the empathic mother-child relationship gives the patient an opportunity to experience consciously the verity that such social interaction is possible. It must, therefore, in varying degrees, provide a model for empathic relatedness on which an important aspect of ethical conduct is built.

The Freudian psychoanalysts are reluctant to deal with questions of ethics and morality either in relation to theory or in the therapeutic situation, fearing the intrusion of subjective values by the analyst, and subscribing to an extreme form of moral relativism. Yet, they cannot avoid the admission[25] that psychoanalytic therapy, even when confined principally to the uncovering of the unconscious, can have an effect on moral conduct. Thus, Hartmann writes: "Still, we cannot write off the cases in which increased self-awareness does have an effect on the moral codes. Broadening of self-knowledge, including also motivations which are commonly unconscious, can lead to a broadening also of the sense of responsibility, the avoidance of easy rationalizations, and so on. Furthermore, it seems likely that a clearer and more objective awareness of motivation and of one's actual value structures also allows a more subtle form of control, which is certainly one of the factors with which we are concerned in considering moral conduct."

This admission, which does inevitably involve the making of a value judgment, in no sense deals with the social consequences of the patient's improved ethical level, much less

---

* Perhaps no psychotherapist has given greater emphasis in her work and writings to the importance of empathy than Frieda Fromm-Reichman. Her influence is explicated by Edith Weigert.[12]

with the effect of these consequences on the evolution of ethics in general. The betterment of moral conduct is never merely an individual matter. Morality, which has its roots in biology and which originated in social interaction during man's sociocultural evolution, is reflected back upon the social scene in all that we know as human thought and behavior. The patient's struggle, therefore, to overcome neurotic difficulties, whether, e.g., symptoms of depression, inhibition, anxiety, or sexual disturbance, and whether he is aware of it or not, is part of a moral and ethical problem to the extent that his insufficiencies are mirrored in his social interactions. The evolutionarily new psychotherapeutic niche, when it is fully and advantageously utilized, could offer the patient the opportunity of resolving his conflicts sufficiently to achieve a new ego synthesis and to participate in the stream of psychosocial evolution as the carrier of a higher level of ethical functioning.

In consulting the therapist, the patient overtly expresses the wish for a better life; but also in so doing he is responding, unbeknown to him, to the great process of psychosocial evolution, of which he is both product and potential catalyst. To respond to this striving, to understand and further it, is the psychotherapist's responsibility and opportunity. The interaction between therapist and patient that ensues demonstrates the play of forces at work in human encounter out of which psychosocial progress may result.

▪ REFERENCES

1. Menaker, E.: Masochism—a defense reaction of the ego. *Psychoanalytic Quarterly 22:* 205-220, 1953.
2. Menaker, E.: A note on some biologic parallels between

certain innate animal behavior and moral masochism. *The Psychoanalytic Review 43:* 31-41, 1956.
3. Jacobson, E.: *The Self and the Object World.* International Universities Press, New York, 1964, pp. 125, 126.
4. Rapaport, D.: *Organization and Pathology of Thought.* Columbia University Press, New York, 1951, p. 518.
5. Freud, S.: *Beyond the Pleasure Principle.* International Psychoanalytic Press, London, Vienna, 1911.
6. Freud, S.: Three essays on the theory of sexuality. *Standard Edition* 7: 125-243, London, Hogarth Press, 1953.
7. Hartmann, H.: *Ego Psychology and the Problem of Adaptation.* International Universities Press, New York, 1958.
8. White, R. W.: *Ego and Reality in Psychoanalytic Theory.* Psychological Issues, Vol. III, No. 3, Monograph 11. International Universities Press, New York, 1963.
9. Rogers, C. R.: The actualizing tendency in relation to "motives" and to consciousness. In Jones, M. R., Ed.: *Nebraska Symposium on Motivation, 1963.* University of Nebraska Press, Lincoln, 1963, pp. 1-23.
10. Erikson, E. H.: *Childhood and Society.* W. W. Norton, New York, 1950, pp. 244-246.
11. Schonbar, R. A.: Transference as a bridge to the future. *American Journal of Psychotherapy XVII:* 290-291, 1963.
12. Weigert, E.: Sympathy, empathy and freedom in therapy. In Salzman, L., and Masserman, J., Eds.: *Modern Concepts of Psychoanalysis.* Citadel Press, New York, 1962, pp. 143, 151, 155.
13. Suttie, I. D.: *The Origins of Love and Hate.* Kegan Paul, Trench, Trubner & Co., Ltd., London, 1935.
14. DeForest, I.: *The Leaven of Love.* Harper & Row, New York, 1954.
15. Storr, A.: *The Integrity of the Personality.* Atheneum, New York, 1961, pp. 119-129.
16. Rank, O.: *Will Therapy and Truth and Reality.* Knopf, New York, 1945, pp. 2, 7-19 (original German publication, 1929).
17. Rogers, Carl R.: *Nebraska Symposium on Motivation,* Ed. Marshall R. Jones. Univ. of Nebraska Press, 1963, pp. 9-14.
18. Jung, C. G.: *Modern Man in Search of a Soul.* Harcourt, Brace, New York, p. 66.

19. Freud, S.: The dynamics of the transference. *Collected Papers*, Vol. II. Hogarth Press, London, 1953, pp. 312-322.
20. Freud, S.: Observations on transference-love. *Collected Papers*, Vol. II. Hogarth Press, London, 1953, pp. 377-391.
21. Sullivan, H. S.: *The Interpersonal Theory of Psychiatry*. W. W. Norton, New York, 1953.
22. Mazer, M.: The therapeutic function of the belief in will. *Psychiatry 23:* 45-52, 1960.
23. Watts, A. W.: *Psychotherapy East and West*. New York, 1961.
24. Von Bertalanffy, L.: *Problems of Life*. Harper & Row, New York, 1960, p. 177.
25. Hartmann, H.: *Psychoanalysis and Moral Values*. International Universities Press, New York, 1960, p. 91.

14 · CONCLUSIONS

IT HAS BEEN our purpose to travel the long way back to the beginnings of life and to discover in these origins and in the gathering momentum of its unfolding in an infinite variety of increasingly complex forms the sources and nature of what is characteristically human. From this vantage point, we have a vast perspective which makes it clear that life as a whole owes its survival to its capacity to evolve. Thus, each species represents a highly evolved manifestation of life within a given environment. The organism and its environment are one interacting, interdependent whole. However, neither aspect of this entirety is static. The environment, whether the physical universe or the existence of other living forms within the organism's biosphere, is ever changing; the organism itself is subject to spontaneous mutational change and to change arising out of developmental processes and interaction with environment. Out of the interaction of this multiplication of changes, the diversity and increasing complexity of organization that we know as evolution transpires. The carrier and transmitter of organic evolutionary advance is the genetic material.

Man makes his appearance at the pinnacle of this evolutionary hierarchy and becomes the dominant species by virtue of the evolution of a brain and nervous system of such complexity as to give rise to consciousness and its organizing principle, ego. We attribute the evolution of consciousness and ego to the same impetus that has been responsible for the progressive development of life from primitive to more complex forms; but with the appearance of consciousness and ego, a new vehicle for evolutionary change has emerged: the vehicle of man's learned, remembered, and transmitted experience as reflected in culture, in the psychological structuring of his being, and in the constant and mutual interaction of these reflections. Thus, human evolution has produced not only new structural and functional advances of the organism itself, but also out of these very advances there has been created a new environment with two interacting facets: the psychological and the social. As the spider spins the thread for his web out of his own body, thus himself creating part of his environment, so man spins the thread of his ego out of its neurophysiological substratum, forming a psychological and subsequently a cultural environment which ultimately reflects back upon the nature of his ego.

The evolution of a new way of evolving through psychosocial transmission has augmented the "openness" of the living system immeasurably. Von Bertalanffy[1] characterizes the living organism "not as a closed system with respect to its sur-roundings but an *open system* which continually gives up matter to the outer world and takes in matter from it." It is the open interchange of matter and energy with the environ-ment that has made evolution possible. Through the emergence of consciousness and memory in man, the possibility for such interchange in quantity, variety, and tempo has been im-measurably augmented and the niche created for the evolu-tion of ego as the integrator and synthesizer of these higher levels of psychic functioning. Through the appearance of ego and its psychological, social, and cultural products, the oppor-tunities for the interaction with environment, for the struc-turing of new environments, both internal and external, and for the transmission of psychosocial gains have been multi-plied a thousandfold.

The habits of language and the history of ideas often leave us a heritage that can be improved upon. So it is with the con-cept of ego, for in some ways it has fallen into ill repute. From its use in philosophy, we inherit the subject-object, body-mind dialectic which leads to metaphysical preoccupations and the confusion of ego, self, soul with that which is beyond the realm of natural phenomena. Psychology, in its ex-perimental and more academic forms, had for a long time dismissed ego as a remnant of psychology's relationship to philosophy. Psychoanalytic psychology, in its theory of man, uses it as a construct to assist in the conceptualization of per-sonality and in the dynamic understanding of neurotic mecha-nisms; and in its therapeutic application, views it as the victim of instinctual forces on the one hand and society on the other. Our emphasis is on a naturalistic conception of ego, conceived for man as the phylogenetically characteristic emergent of his evolutionary history: the result of the evolution of brain and nervous system, out of which appeared the mental, whose continuous interaction with external and internal environments created culture, structured personality, and a new vehicle for further psychosocial evolution.

When we were children, being instructed in the nature of our planet, our geography teachers were very eager to make it clear that the equator was but an *imaginary* line. Certainly, no one would dispute this fact. Yet, the equator is a reality, as an expression of relationships of positions in space. No one would deny the geographic palpability of this mathematical co-ordinate. Ego is similarly a co-ordinate which expresses a relationship of processes, i.e., neurophysiological processes resulting in awareness, with bodily, cognitive, and emotional processes within the organism, and with physical, social, and cultural processes in the external environment. Its reality is perceptible in its co-ordinating function which makes of all reality an inner subjective experience. This, then, would be the psychobiological definition of ego with which we would hope to replace either static psychological constructs or metaphysical conceptions.

Ego not only *has* evolved, but as an aspect of reality *is* evolving. Here, the statement of Julian Huxley[2] is most appropriate: "All reality, in fact, is evolution, in the perfectly proper sense that it is a one-way process in time: unitary, continuous, irreversible, self-transforming and generating variety and novelty during its transformations." There are, of course, regressions in the life cycle of individual egos, but in the large psychobiological sense, ego is evolving. This becomes manifest in the history of culture, in which we not only encounter progress in the mastery of nature, the development of social institutions, and the creation of art forms, but also in the very character and quality of ego itself, in the sharpness of its definition, in its capacity for relatedness and empathy, for creativity and expressiveness, for humor, play, craftsmanship, and for satisfaction in the competent fulfillment of these functions.

On the human level, the struggle for survival has been largely replaced, as Huxley would say, "by the struggle for fulfillment." We would say that fulfillment is an essential aspect of psychological survival. For man, the striving toward fulfillment is an ego striving toward a harmonious relationship between all aspects of his environment, inner and outer, and his own being—a harmony which would let him feel himself part of the evolutionary stream of life while at the same time experiencing his own individuation.

In all his endeavors to mold and master environment—in his social, cultural, and religious institutions, in his aesthetic and scientific endeavors and in his human relationships—man attempts to approximate this ideal of fulfillment.*

However, striving, struggle, and conflict, as well as gratification and fulfillment, are the subjective, affective reflections of man's ongoing processes of psychological evolution. Neither his individual ontogenous development nor the evolutionary course of human history proceeds without upheavals and regressions. The task of resolving conflict, whether individual or societal, and of giving meaning to life, since he must live it with awareness, has been man's concern from the beginning of his history. From the objective standpoint of his organic evolution, man has succeeded: His number has increased (even to the point of its being a threat to his survival and therefore in itself a problem to be resolved), and he is the dominant species. From the standpoint of his psychosocial evolution, man is sometimes uncertain about the meaning of what he has achieved in terms of adaptation and about his capacities for further evolution. Such uncertainty has its

---

* Different societies offer varying opportunities for fulfillment.

origin in the spectacle of the catastrophic and tragic social events of human history—for contemporary man, the wars, persecutions, destructions, and crimes of the last half century —and in the fact that man must subjectively experience an adaptation that includes a knowledge of his own death.

Freud[3] attempted a biological explanation of the human dilemma in terms of his instinct theory. According to him, the motivating principle determining human behavior is the need for the discharge of tensions created by the instinctual impulses. The need for such discharge is inevitably in conflict with the demands of society, especially as it applies to sexual and aggressive drives. Man is condemned therefore to an irresolvable problem posed by the seemingly contradictory nature of his instinctual needs and the need for a social structure in order to survive. This is reflected in his personal neuroticisms and his societal maladjustments. This pessimistic conclusion brings man to a dead end in evolutionary terms.

We have tried to show that the common phylogenetic origin of instinct and society means that they must interact to serve the survival needs of the species, and that individual or societal disequilibrium, as expressed in human conflict, is a by-product of man's ongoing psychosocial evolution rather than a result of two separate and irreconcilable aspects of his nature. The vehicle for such evolution is ego, the organizer of consciousness, which is always open to new experience, to a recombination and re-evaluation of all that it has known and experienced, and to new ways of relating to others.

Yet, man's species-characteristic instruments of survival, consciousness and ego, their expansion and ongoing evolution, present him with special problems. The mastery of the external environment, i.e., both physical and social reality, and of his inner psychological environment is predicated on the peculiar and particular nature of human consciousness through which external reality is internalized by conceptual verbal symbols. Ego then organizes these symbols into a meaningful whole. When they are organized into an aesthetic relationship, man creates art in some form; when they are organized into a causal relationship, man arrives at an understanding of his world. In pure survival terms, therefore, there is a biological necessity to understand reality in causal terms. However, when man attempts to turn causal thinking to an understanding of his position in the universe, he is constrained to find meaning in life, to explain the inevitable anxieties, pains, frustrations, and deprivations of life in terms of purpose, or at least of a meaningful causality. Thus, systems of thought arise that attempt to answer the question of purpose, of meaning.

Throughout man's cultural history, they are represented by philosophies, religions, political systems, psychoanalysis, science as system. However, the question of meaning or purpose in life, motivation for life, is a teleological one which cannot be answered in terms of causality, but only in terms of belief or by an abrogation of the question itself and an acceptance of existence for its own sake.

The search for meaning is the ego's attempt to understand its place in the universe, to integrate and co-ordinate its relationship to the continuum of life. This search has itself gone through evolutionary stages which represent a hierarchical advance in the approximation between belief and a causal understanding of natural phenomena. This means that the nature of religion, which has in the main provided man with an answer to the meaning of his existence, must inevitably undergo a change from its more illusory form to one approximating man's grasp of reality.

Since man has evolved so as to vest in ego the survival function, and since the ego perceives itself as a part of reality, it seeks an explanation for its existence that is commensurate with its grasp of environmental causality. As his mastery and understanding of the environment increase, it becomes increasingly difficult to synthesize a religious or philosophical belief concerning his being with a causal grasp of reality. The very structure or process, ego, on whose ability to organize experience and understanding, survival and evolution depend, cannot answer a teleological question regarding purpose because such a question can never be a biological one. Yet, the habits of thought which derive from the awareness of control of environment and from choice of action in the motivation of an ontogenous act lead the ego to attempt an answer.

We see man's dilemma then, and his attempts to solve it through religion for example, not solely as a reaction to an emotional feeling of helplessness deriving from the pedamorphic experience of infancy and a corresponding wish to return to it,[4] but as the inevitable by-product of the contradictions that arise between his phylogenetically evolved awareness and its organizer, ego, because of the limitations of the ontogenous ego in closing the gap between a causal understanding of environment and a meaningful understanding of life.

It is, however, precisely this contradiction which creates the evolutionary impetus for new levels of ego organization. Man has given meaning to his life in religious belief, ideologies, and the creation and nurture of the social institutions which represent these. He has internalized this meaning intrapsychically in the form of his ego-ideal. It is in this process that man's spiritual nature is revealed as a psychobiological inevitability. He has internalized experience in all its aspects in terms of his mental symbols: visual, verbal, conceptual. A panoramic view of man's cultural history reveals the evolutionary history of ego through a consistent narrowing of the gap between external reality and the inner symbols that express it; the symbols approximate the reality more closely;

the gap between illusion and reality is thereby lessened. This is the essence of scientific discovery. The evolution of social institutions, religion, ethics, and government reveals an evolution of the ego-ideal which moves in the direction of an increasing regard for the autonomy of the individual ego.

Ego evolution thus closes the gap increasingly between illusion—whether in the form of a symbolic representation of the outer world or in an attempt to give meaning to life through a specific ego-ideal—and reality. In this way, higher levels of ego autonomy and clearer delineation of ego are achieved; with them, an increasing capacity to interrelate with others on a mature basis, i.e., to love, evolves.

Does the inclusion of the awareness of his own evolution mean, for man, that he can from now on become the master of his own further evolution? Certainly, this is the implication in psychosocial terms as expressed by evolutionary thinkers such as C. J. Herrick, Julian Huxley, and T. Dobzhansky. They have set up goals for mankind, in the form of the advancement of democratic institutions and the control of world population, that are essential to man's survival and evolutionary progress. That men of science should bring to bear on human welfare the fruits of their insights and knowledge and thus express their concern with values is a more or less contemporary phenomenon. It is in itself an evolutionary answer to the need created by the threat to man's survival resulting from the discovery of atomic weapons and by the uncontrolled growth of human populations. Yet, it is of the utmost importance to be aware that once such goals become "utopian" and "finalistic" they lose their evolutionary validity. For evolution knows no "solutions" in an absolute sense; it knows only change that hopefully is appropriate to a given set of circumstances. Thus, to attempt a control of man's evolution without a perspective on the factor of *inevitability* residing in the ongoing, future-directed adaptational process that is evolution is to proceed in a way that is essentially anti-evolutionary. All systems of thought that are "perfectionistic," whether theories of evolution, social and political ideologies, or religious systems, by virtue of their rigidity and finality of goal, run counter to the evolutionary process. They may, however, through their content, contribute to human advance.

Consciously arrived at goals aimed at controlling man's evolution must therefore be conceived of as way-stations in a directional process, not as ultimate solutions. "In fact evolution means continuity of change; and the fact that change may take the form of present growth of complexity and interaction. Significant stages in change are found not in access of fixity of attainment but in those crises in which a seeming fixity of habits gives way to a release of capacities that have not previously functioned; in times, that is, of readjustment and redirection."[5]

The anxiety created by the conflict between the fear of evolving and the wish to evolve, in social, psychological, and especially in ego terms, which is sometimes experienced consciously but generally is an unconscious aspect of the life process, leads man to set up finalistic goals in the hope that once he achieves them he will transcend the problem of adaptation. Such a hope can never be fulfilled, however. For all living beings, adaptation is not absolutely guaranteed in the sense that it is always dependent on, and relative to specific environmental circumstances. Yet, for man this guarantee, in the shadow of his anxiety, seems even more fragile, since he himself, in full awareness and through his own ego efforts, must assume the responsibility for his adaptation. However, this seeming burden is also an opportunity. Within the social stream, individuals, in varying degrees, will perceive the general direction of psychosocial evolution as it emerges from all that has gone before, and will lend assistance to its forward movement. The potentiality for man's total destruction through the use of atomic weapons has alerted him to his evolutionary responsibility more fully than ever before. As evolving human beings, can we fail to believe that ultimately his ego will be equal to the task?

▪ **REFERENCES**

1. Von Bertalanffy, L.: *Problems of Life.* Harper & Row, New York, 1960, p. 125.
2. Huxley, J.: *Evolution in Action.* Harper & Row, New York, 1953, p. 2.
3. Freud, S.: *Civilization and Its Discontents.* Doubleday, New York, 1958.
4. Freud, S.: *The Future of an Illusion.* Liveright, New York, 1949.
5. Dewey, J.: *Human Nature and Conduct.* Random House, New York, 1922, p. 284.

▪ INDEX

Abel, 165, 166

Actualizing of ego functions, 222, 223
(see also Ego)

Adaptability, 33
hierarchy of, 79

Adaptation, 31, 51n, 65, 66, 80, 229,
239, 240, 244
cultural, 66
of ego, 229
and evolution of nervous processes
and tissue, 50
higher levels of, 228
increased control of environment,
34
as integration with environment,
33
mutual, between mother and child,
162
plasticity of, 34
as specialization, 33
for survival, 34

Adaptive efficacy, 122

Adaptive need, 6

Adaptive potential, 33, 34

Adler, Alfred, 18

Admiralty Islands, 60n

Advance, 76
in complexity of organization, 33
creates pressure for new adaptations, 183
in efficiency, 33
ethical, 70
in evolution, 32
in equalitarian ideas, 70
in human relatedness, 70
manifest in higher levels of ego
integration, 180

in relation to increased capacity to
survive and reproduce, 33
technological and scientific, 70

Aesthetic creativity, 181n

Affect(s), neurophysiological and
mentational, 144

Affection, 61

Affectional bond, 95

Affectional response system, 124
(see also Mother)

Affective experiences, 214

Afferent impulses, 125

Affirmative anticipation, 132n

Agar, W. E., 89

Age of Enlightenment, 63

Age of Reason, 63

Aggressive impulses, 7

Aggressive instinct, 172

Albanian children, 20

America, psychoanalytic discoveries
in, 96

American Army, 60n

American culture, 200

American egalitarianism, 60n

American life, 69n

American professional woman, 107

Amnesia(s) of childhood, 214

Amoeba, 33

Anal phase, 216

Angyal, A., 177, 185

Anxiety, 7, 41, 93, 97, 98, 100, 102,
105-110, 125, 143-161, 179, 180,
201, 220, 225, 229, 232, 244

247